D1631844

NATIVE AMERICAN
MYTHS & LEGENDS

* * *

This book is dedicated to Joseph Keena

First published in Great Britain by Brockhampton Press, a member of the Hodder Headline Group,
20 Bloomsbury Street, London WC1B 3QA.

Copyright © 1998 Brockhampton Press.

ISBN 1 86019 377 3

A copy of the CIP data is available from the British Library upon request.

Created and produced by Flame Tree Publishing, a part of The Foundry Creative Media Company Limited,
The Long House, Antrobus Road, Chiswick, London W4 5HY.

NATIVE AMERICAN
MYTHS & LEGENDS

O. B. DUANE

CONTENTS

INTRODUCTION

HE WHITE MAN'S FIRST ENCOUNTER with the native aboriginal population of America dates back to the year 1000 AD, almost five hundred years before the Genoese explorer Christopher Columbus crossed the Atlantic. A group of Norsemen, sailing from Norway to Greenland, was thrown off course in rough weather conditions and soon came in sight of a land of which they had no previous knowledge. The 'Land of Flat Stones', as the adventurers called it, was what came to be called Newfoundland, a barren country whose inhospitable appearance prompted them to sail further south. Soon they approached the low, tree-covered country of what is now Nova Scotia, and named it 'Mark-land'. Sailing still farther south, they came upon a land where the air was warmer, whose soil had produced fields of self-sown wheat and vines laden with ripened grapes. The Norsemen had arrived on the shores of New England and before long they had christened it 'Wine-land'.

Impressed by their welcoming surroundings, they embarked upon a bold attempt to colonize the newly discovered country; but fate decreed that the hostility of several bands of swarthy natives should check this expansion. Soon, the Vikings were subjected to repeated attacks by men they nicknamed 'Skrellings' or 'Chips' owing to their stunted, puny appearance. It was these inhabitants, possessing Eskimo characteristics, who brought about the destruction of the Scandinavian settlements and an end to colonial activity until the arrival of the European settlers in the wake of Columbus's discovery of the West Indian islands.

So who exactly were these strange people the Norsemen encountered, and where had they come from? The name 'Indian', which for many centuries has been used to describe the native aboriginal population of America, is actually a misnomer and owes its origin to Christopher Columbus who believed he had discovered a new route to Asiatic India when he landed in the Caribbean islands in 1492. Once this error had been acknowledged, however, other equally spurious theories on the origin of the race began to emerge. Some theorists traced the native American people back to Egypt, to the South Sea Islands, and even to Wales. Others were intent on proving a connection between the American 'Indian' and the Lost Tribes of Israel.

Opposite:
Early villages had much in common with Eskimo and Asian settlements joined by the ancient landlink now called the Bering Straits.

Their rype corne.

Their greene corne.

Corne newly sprong.

Their sitting at meale

The place wherin they make their Prayer

...rose wherin the Tombe of their Herounds standeth.

Most scientists nowadays are agreed that the 'Indians' of the Americas arrived in the New World as immigrants, forced to migrate southwards during the last great ice age over twenty thousand years ago. The physical similarities between the 'Indian' and the Eskimo point to northern Asia as his original home and it is now almost certain that he would have crossed from Alaska to America via the Bering Strait, a land bridge a thousand miles wide once linking Asia and America. When this land bridge became submerged in the melting ice, the 'Indian' found himself stranded in this new homeland and eventually spread out to inhabit all of North, Central and South America.

The first native American people were already competent hunters and gatherers. They were skilled in the making of warm clothing from animal skins and understood the use of fire. Armed with tools of stone, bone, antler and wood, they hunted the great Pleistocene animals, including mammoths, camelops and superbison, surviving almost exclusively on this plentiful supply of meat. Later, when the big game began to disappear, the 'Indian' started to exploit other food sources, learning to cultivate the land to produce fruit and vegetables, seeds and nuts. Many who inhabited areas where soil and climate were good, discovered they no longer needed to move on in search of game and wild food and began to form more permanent communities. Others continued to maintain their nomadic lifestyle, either hunting or challenging others for whatever they needed to survive. By the time white explorers began arriving in America in the early sixteenth century, the descendants of the original settlers were divided into numerous different tribes, most of them self-sufficient, with their own individual language and customs. It has been estimated, for example, that no less than five hundred languages existed north of Mexico at this time.

Fringing the shores of the Northern Ocean, from the Siberian shore of the Bering Sea in the west to the Gulf of St Lawrence in the east, were the Eskimos, the connecting link between the races of the Old and New Worlds. The name 'Eskimo' means 'raw meat eaters' and these were a carnivorous body of hunters, speaking a distinct language. They differed also in physical appearance from the 'Indian', being of short, stocky build, with a long head, short face and a well-marked Mongol eyefold.

Opposite: By the time white explorers arrived the descendants of the original 'Indians' were divided into numerous different tribes, each with its own individual language and customs.

South of the Eskimos, extending in a broad band across the continent from the Hudson Bay to the Pacific, and southwards almost to the Great Lakes, were the Athapascan stock. These tribes spread as far north as the mouth of the Mackenzie River,

but also covered a huge area in the opposite direction, migrating south along the Rocky Mountains, where they scattered themselves over the plains of New Mexico under the names of Apaches and Navajos.

The most well-known to us of the native American people, the Algonquins and Iroquois, originally occupied the entire region of what is now Canada and the eastern coast of the United States, extending as far south as Virginia. These two groups are the main focus of this book and a selection of their myths and tales, drawn from various tribes, follow in the next two sections.

The Muskhogean Indians, including the Choctaws, Chickasaws, Creeks and Seminoles, originally possessed almost all of Mississippi and Alabama, portions of Tennessee, Florida and South Carolina. Their neighbours to the west were the Dakota Indians, including the Sioux and Winnebagoes. A tall, lithe people, the Dakotas found an agricultural lifestyle uncongenial, but they were recognized as the champion warriors of the native American population. Deeply religious, with a strict moral code, they originally occupied a territory extending from Saskatchewan to Louisiana.

The Caddoan family consisted of a federation of tribes living along the Platte River in what is now the state of Nebraska. They included the Arikara, Pawnee, Caddo, Kichai and Wichita tribes. These peoples were agriculturalists as well as hunters and practised pottery-making and hide tanning.

Living alongside the Caddoan to the west were the Shoshonean, or Snake, family of North American 'Indians', comprising, among others, the Root-diggers, Comanches, Kiowas and Hopi. They originally occupied the great desert region between the Wasatch Mountains and the Sierra Nevada.

The Shoshonean Indians were flanked by the Salishan, Californian and Piman 'Indians'. The Salishan, probably of Algonquian stock, occupied territories of Washington. The Californian, including the Cahrocs, Pericues and Olchones, were a loose conglomeration speaking a variety of different languages, while the Pimans were traditional farmers occupying land in southern Arizona and along the western coast.

Opposite:
The Algonquins and Iroquois, originally occupied the whole of what is now Canada and the eastern coast of the United States, extending as far south as Virginia.

Cut off from the rest of the world, the native American did not suffer the dilution of blood and culture which modified the nations of the Old World. This situation no doubt contributed to the fact that as soon as the New World was discovered, its inhabitants became a source of fascination to all classes of Europeans. When these white settlers came, they were generally welcomed by the

natives, but soon the 'Indian' discovered that the white man could not be trusted and came to regard the colonizer as the intruder. Treating the natives as savages, the white man took for himself whatever property he considered of value and ruthlessly exploited the natural resources of the land so precious to the native population.

The European invasion brought not only more wars over land and food, but cultural and religious conflict, as well as diseases previously unknown in North America. The changes were dramatic and ultimately disastrous for the 'Indian'. Within a few years of their landing, the whites had freed New England of these 'harmless natives', and as more and more Europeans arrived, the face of native American culture was altered forever. The 'Indian' fought against the invaders as best he could but, step by step, he was driven westwards until he had all but vanished from his ancestral lands. By the late nineteenth century, the United States Government had implemented a policy of housing 'Indian' survivors on tracts of land known as reservations, where many still live today, effectively ending the existence of tribes as independent communities.

The native American people have little to thank the white man for, but among the white traders and missionaries there were at least some with the foresight to attempt to preserve the unique oral heritage they happened upon. Today's native American people have lost many of their customs and beliefs, but a number of the old traditions have been consecrated in their mythology, allowing us a rewarding insight into the way the New World must once have looked and felt to its original inhabitants. It is a world we cannot possibly enter, however, without feeling a profound sense of shame and loss.

✼   ✼   ✼

AUTHOR'S NOTE

The myths and legends retold in this book have been selected from among the folklore of the native American tribes of North America and represent only a tiny proportion of the vast number of tales in existence. The mythology of the Central or South American 'Indians', although equally important, would demand one, if not two more books. This volume is intended to provide an enjoyable and entertaining introduction to the most popular myths and fables of the native Americans of the North and is in no way a comprehensive study of its subject. None the less, it is hoped that the stories included will inspire and encourage the reader to explore this compelling subject further. The book focuses on the native Americans as they were, and not as they are. Because of this, the more traditional term 'Indian' is frequently applied, particularly in the stories themselves.

MYTHS OF
THE IROQUOIS PEOPLE

HE IROQUOIS, WHOSE NAME MEANS 'real adders', were perhaps the most resilient and hostile of the native American Indian population, demonstrating a rare political prowess. A race of born warriors, they originally occupied the north-eastern woodlands stretching from the Lake Ontario region as far southwards as Tennessee, Pennsylvania and Virginia. They were leading figures in the early colonial wars against the white settlers, although they eventually made friends with the English and the Dutch, using them to crush their old enemies, the Algonquins.

The League of the Iroquois, which was probably formed around 1570, bonded together five powerful tribes – the Mohawk, Oneida, Onondaga, Cayuga and Seneca. Later the Tuscarora joined this league, allowing the Iroquois to develop a huge sphere of political and cultural influence at the height of their power, unlike the Algonquins whose greatest weakness was a lack of tribal solidity.

Myths and legends of the Iroquois people are of particular interest for their semi-historical portraits. Hiawatha, the great warrior responsible for uniting the feuding tribes, has been immortalized in this manner, alongside Atotarho, the mighty Onondaga chief, who appears in Iroquois legend as a mythical king, clothed in black snakes. In common with other native American races, the Iroquois worshipped a number of deities, including Tahahiawagon – he who comes from the Sky. They held a strong belief in witchcraft and were convinced of the existence of a number of malevolent beings roaming the earth, among them the Stone Giants and the curious creature known as Great Head.

Creation Myth of the Iroquois

AT THE DAWN OF CREATION, before mankind ever existed, the universe comprised two separate worlds. The lower world was a place of eternal darkness, peopled only by creatures of the water, while the upper world, a kingdom of bright light, was inhabited by the Great Ruler and his family. The goddess Atahensic was daughter of the Great Ruler, and at this time she was heavy with child and very close to her time of confinement. As the hour drew near, her relatives persuaded her to lie down on a soft mattress, wrapping her in a ray of light, so that her weary body would gather strength and refreshment for the task ahead. But as soon as she had closed her eyes, the bed on which she lay began to sink without warning through the thick clouds, plunging rapidly towards the lower world beneath her.

Dazzled and alarmed by the descending light, the monsters and creatures of the great water held an emergency council to decide what should be done.

'If the being from above falls on us,' said the Water-hen, 'it will surely destroy us. We must quickly find a place where it can rest.'

'Only the oeh-da, the Earth which lies at the very bottom of the water, will be strong enough to hold it,' said the Beaver. 'I will swim down and bring some back with me.' But the Beaver never returned from his search.

Then the Duck volunteered himself for the same duty, but soon his dead body floated up to the surface. Finally, however, the Muskrat came forward:

'I know the way better than anyone,' he told the others, 'but the oeh-da is extremely heavy and will grow very fast. Who is prepared to bear its weight when I appear with it?'

The Turtle, who was by far the most capable among them, readily agreed to suffer the load. Shortly afterwards, the Muskrat returned with a small quantity of the oeh-da in his paw which he smoothed on to the turtle's back. It began to spread rapidly, and as soon as it had reached a satisfactory size for the light to rest on, two birds soared into the air and bore the goddess on their outstretched wings down towards the water and safely on to the turtle's back. From that day onwards, the Turtle became known as the Earth Bearer, and whenever the seas rise up in great waves, the people know that it is the Turtle stirring in his bed.

A considerable island of earth now floated on the waves,

Opposite: All over the land, the Good Mind formed creeks and rivers, valleys and hills. He created animals to inhabit the forests and filled the seas with fishes and mammals.

providing a timely shelter, for soon Atahensic began to hear two voices within her womb, one soft and soothing, the other loud and aggressive, and she knew that her mission to people the island was close at hand. The conflict continued within, as one of her twin infants sought to pass out under the side of his mother's arm, while the other held him back, attempting to spare his mother this unnecessary pain. Both entered into the world in their own individual way, the first bringing trouble and strife, the second bringing freedom and peace. The goddess wisely accepted that it must be so, and named her children Hahgwehdiyu, meaning Good Mind, and Hahgwehdaetgah, meaning Bad Mind. Each went his way, Hahgwehdiyu anxious to bring beauty to the island, Hahgwehdaetgah determined that darkness and evil should prevail.

Not long after she had given birth, Atahensic passed away and the island grew dim in the dawn of its new life. Knowing the goddess would not have wished it this way, Hahgwehdiyu lifted his palm high into the air and began moulding the sky with his fingers. After he had done this, he took his mother's head from her body and placed it firmly in the centre of the firmament:

'You shall be known as the Sun', he announced, 'and your face shall light up this new world where you shall rule forever.'

But his brother saw all of this good work and set darkness in the west sky, forcing the Sun down behind it. Hahgwehdiyu would not be beaten, however, and removing a portion of his mother's breast, he cast it upwards, creating an orb, inferior to the sun, yet capable of illuminating the darkness. Then he surrounded the orb with numerous spots of light, giving them the name of stars and ordering them to regulate the days, nights, seasons and years. When he had completed this work above, he turned his attention to the soil beneath his feet. To the barren earth he gave the rest of his mother's body from which the seeds of all future life were destined to spring forth.

The Good Mind continued the works of creation, refusing all rest until he had accomplished everything he had set out to do. All over the land he formed creeks and rivers, valleys and hills, luscious pastures and evergreen forests. He created numerous species of animals to inhabit the forests, from the smallest to the greatest, and filled the seas and lakes with fishes and mammals of every variety and colour. He appointed thunder to water the earth and winds to scatter pollen so that, in time, the island became fruitful and productive. But all was not yet complete, for

Hahgwehdiyu wisely observed that a greater being was needed to take possession of the Great Island. And so, he began forming two images from the dust of the ground in his own likeness. To these he gave the name of Eagwehowe, meaning the Real People, and by breathing into their nostrils he gave them living souls.

When the earth was created and Hahgwehdiyu had bestowed a protective spirit upon every object of his creation, he went out in search of his brother, hoping to persuade him to abandon his evil and vicious existence; but the Bad Mind was already hard at work, intent on destroying all evidence of Hahgwehdiyu's remarkable labour. Without much effort, he overcame the guardian spirits he encountered and marched throughout the island, bending the rivers, sundering the mountains, gnarling the forests and destroying food crops. He created lethal reptiles to injure mankind, led ferocious monsters into the sea and gathered great hurricanes in the sky. Still dissatisfied with the devastation, however, he began making two images of clay in the form of humans, aiming to create a more superior and destructive race. But he was quickly made to realize that he had not been blessed with the same creative powers as the Good Mind, for as he breathed life into them, his clay figures turned into hideous apes. Infuriated by this discovery, the Bad Mind thundered through the island like a terrible whirlwind, uprooting fruit-trees and wringing the necks of animals and birds. Only one thing would now satisfy his anger, a bloody and ruthless combat to the death, and with this purpose in mind, he hastened towards his twin-brother's dwelling.

Weary of the destruction he had witnessed, the Good Mind willingly submitted himself to the contest that would decide the ruler of the earth. The Bad Mind was keen to discover anything that might help to destroy his brother's temporal life and began to question him rather slyly on the type of weapons they should use.

'Tell me,' he said, 'what particular instrument would cause you the most injury, so that I may avoid its use, as a gesture of goodwill.'

Hahgwehdiyu could see through this evil strategy, however, and falsely informed him that he would certainly be struck down by a lotus arrow.

'There is nothing I fear,' the Bad Mind boasted, but Hahgwehdiyu knew this to be untrue, and wisely remembered that ever since childhood the horns of a stag had always induced feelings of terror in his brother.

The battle began and lasted for two days and two nights, causing panic and disruption throughout the earth as mountains shook violently under the strain of the combat and rivers overflowed with the blood of both brothers. At last, however, the Bad Mind could no longer ignore the temptation to shoot the lotus arrow in his brother's direction. The Good Mind responded by charging at him with the stag-horns, impaling him on their sharp points until he screamed in pain and fell to the ground begging for mercy.

Hahgwehdiyu, the supreme ruler of the earth, immediately banished his evil brother to a dark pit beneath the surface of the world, ordering him never to return. Gathering together as many hideous beasts and monsters as he could find, he flung them below so that they might share with their creator a life of eternal doom. Some escaped his grasp, however, and remained on the earth as Servers, half-human and half-beasts, eager to continue the destructive work of the Bad Mind who had now become known as the Evil Spirit.

Hahgwehdiyu, faithful to the wishes of his grandfather, the Great Ruler, carried on with his good work on the floating island, filling the woodlands with game, slaying the monsters, teaching the Indians to make fires and to raise crops, and instructing them in many of the other arts of life until the time had come for him to retire from the earth to his celestial home.

The Origin of Medicine

IN THE OLD DAYS, there was peace throughout the earth and mankind lived in friendship and harmony with the great beasts of creation. But as time progressed, the human race multiplied rapidly and became so large that the animals were forced to surrender their settlements and seek out new homes in the forests and deserts. Although cramped and unhappy, they did not complain too vociferously, but embraced these changes with an open mind, hoping that mankind would now remain satisfied. Sadly, however, this was not the case, and within a short time, man began to equip himself with a variety of weapons – bows, arrows, axes, spears and hooks – which he used to attack the beasts of the forests, slaughtering them for their flesh and valuable skins.

Opposite:
Although the animals attempted to live in peace with the human race, man equipped himself with weapons which he used to attack and slaughter them.

The animals, at first incredulous, soon became enraged by this show of bloodthirsty contempt and began to consider measures that would guarantee them their survival and safety. The bear tribe was the first to meet in council under Kuwahi mountain, presided over

by White Bear, their chief. One after another, members of the tribe stood up and reported the appalling atrocities their families had suffered. Mankind had mutilated their bodies, devoured their flesh, skinned them to make superfluous clothing and displayed their severed heads on wooden stakes as trophies. There was only one way to deal with such hostility, it was unanimously agreed, and it involved wholesale war.

The bears sat down to deliberate their strategy more seriously, but as soon as someone asked about weapons, they all fell silent, knowing that humans had one distinct advantage over them in this respect.

'We should turn man's own instruments upon him,' announced one of the elder bears. 'Let us go and find one of these bows, together with some arrows, and copy their design.'

A messenger returned shortly afterwards with these objects and the group gathered round to examine them carefully. A strong piece of locust wood was called for by the chief and with this he constructed a bow. Then, one of the younger bears provided a piece of his gut for the string and soon the weapon was completed, ready for its first testing.

The strongest, most agile bear volunteered his services. He had little trouble drawing back the bow, but as soon as he attempted to let the arrow fly, his long claws became entangled in the string and the shot was ruined. He quickly realized that he would have to trim his claws, and when he had done this, he let a second arrow fly which hit its target successfully. Delighted with himself, he turned to face the chief, but White Bear did not appear at all pleased by the result.

'We need our claws to climb trees,' he wisely proclaimed. 'If we cut off our claws we will not be able to climb or hunt down prey and soon we would all starve together.' And saying this, he ordered the group to scatter amongst the woods, instructing them to reappear before him when they had found a better solution.

The deer also held a similar council under their chief, Little Deer. After they had aired their grievances and lamented the death of their comrades, they came to a decision that if any human hunter should attempt to slay one of them without first asking suitable pardon, he would be struck down by rheumatism. Notice of this decision was sent out to all the Indian villages nearby and the people were instructed what to do if ever necessity demanded that they kill one of the deer tribe.

So now, whenever a deer is hit by an arrow, Little Deer, who moves faster than the wind and can never be wounded, runs to the

Opposite: The animals, at first incredulous, soon became enraged by their cruel treatment. One after another they stood up and reported the appalling atrocities they had suffered.

spot where the victim has fallen and, bending over the pool of blood, asks the spirit of the deer whether or not he has heard the hunter's plea for pardon. If the reply is 'yes', the hunter remains fit and well, but if the answer is 'no', then Little Deer tracks him to his cabin and strikes him down with rheumatism, transforming him into a helpless cripple.

The fishes and reptiles were the next to gather together to determine an appropriate punishment for their aggressors. They held a council which lasted only a few minutes, where it was quickly decided that those who tortured or killed any of their species would be tormented by nightmarish visions of slimy serpents with foul breath twining around their limbs and throats, very slowly choking them to death. Or else, these brutal attackers would dream, day and night, of eating raw, decaying fish, causing them to refuse all food and to sicken and die as a result.

Finally, the birds, insects and smaller animals held their own meeting, presided over by a grub-worm. Each creature, he announced, should come forward and state his point of view and if the consensus was against mankind, the entire race should be put to death by the most cruel and painful means.

Frog was the first to leap forward and he delivered his tirade in a loud and angry voice:

'Something will have to be done to stop the spread of this human menace,' he thundered. 'See how they have kicked me and beaten me with sticks because they think I'm ugly. Now my back is covered with sores that will never disappear.' And he pointed to the spots on his skin for everyone around him to examine.

Next a group of birds hopped forward and began to condemn mankind for the way in which he ruthlessly set out to burn their feet, impaling them on a stick over a fire as soon as he had trapped them, and turning them slowly until their claws and feathers were singed black.

Others then followed with a string of complaints and criticisms, so that apart from the ground-squirrel, who had seldom been a victim because of his tiny size, there was not one among the gathering who showed any restraint or compassion towards the human species. Hurriedly, they began to devise and name various lethal diseases to be released among the human population. As the list grew longer, the grub-worm shook with laughter and glee, until he suddenly fell over backwards and could not rise to his feet again, but had to wriggle off on his back, as he has done ever since that day.

Opposite:
In time, every tribe boasted a shaman, capable of hearing the spirit-voices of the plants speaking to him whenever he was in doubt about a cure.

Only the plants remained friendly towards man, and before long every tree, shrub and herb, down even to the wild grasses and mosses, agreed to provide some remedy for the diseases now hanging thick in the air.

'We will help mankind in his hour of need,' each plant affirmed. 'Every one of us shall assist in the struggle against sickness and disease and hope that in return, the earth will be restored to order.'

Even the weeds in the fields were endowed with healing properties and, in time, every tribe boasted a shaman, a great healer, capable of hearing the spirit-voices of the plants speaking to him whenever he was in doubt about a cure.

It was in this way that the very first medicine came into being, ensuring the survival of a human race which had come so perilously close to destruction.

The Legend of Hiawatha

A GREAT MANY FANCIFUL MYTHS AND LEGENDS have sprung up around Hiawatha, the famous Iroquois warrior and chief. Such a tradition is demonstrated, for example, by H. W. Longfellow, whose poem, Hiawatha, combines historical fact and mythical invention to produce a highly colourful demi-god figure akin to the Algonquin deity, Michabo. The real Hiawatha, an actual historical figure, lived in the sixteenth century and was renowned for promoting a very down-to-earth policy of tribal union. His greatest achievement was the formation of the original Five Nations Confederacy of the Iroquois people. The legend chosen here, although it too reveres Hiawatha as a man of mystical qualities, is based on that historical accomplishment and has been adapted from a story told by a nineteenth-century Onondaga chief.

Along the banks of Tioto, or Cross Lake as it was often called, there lived an eminent young warrior named Hiawatha. Also known as the Wise Man throughout the district, he exerted a powerful influence over the people. No one knew exactly where Hiawatha had come from. They knew only that he was of a high and mysterious origin and investigated no further than this. He had a canoe, controlled by his will, which could move without the aid of paddles, but he did not use it for any common purpose and pushed it out into the water only when he attended the general council of the tribes.

It was from Hiawatha that the villagers sought advice when they attempted to raise corn and beans. As a direct result of his instruction, their crops flourished; even after they had harvested the corn, food was never in short supply for he taught them how to remove obstructions from watercourses and to clear their fishing grounds. The people listened to Hiawatha with ever-increasing respect, and as he continued to provide them with wise laws and proverbs for their development, they came to believe that he had been sent by the Great Spirit himself, for a short but precious stay amongst them.

After a time, Hiawatha elected to join the Onondagas tribe and it was not long before he had been elevated to a prime position of authority, next in line to its chief.[1] The Onondagas enjoyed a long period of peace and prosperity under Hiawatha's guidance, and there was not one among the other tribes of the region that did not yield to their superiority.

But then, one day, a great alarm was suddenly raised among the entire people of the region. From north of the Great Lakes, a ferocious band of warriors advanced towards them[2], destroying whatever property they could lay their hands on and indiscriminately slaughtering men, women and children. Everyone looked to Hiawatha for comfort and advice and, as a first measure, he called together a council of all the tribes from the east to the west and appointed a time for a meeting to take place on the banks of the Onondaga Lake.

By midday, a great body of men, women and children had gathered together in anticipation that they would shortly experience some form of deliverance. But after they had waited several hours they became anxious to know what had become of Hiawatha, for he appeared to be nowhere in sight. Three days elapsed and still Hiawatha did not appear. The crowd, beginning to fear that he was not coming at all, despatched a group of messengers to his home and here they found him sitting on the ground, seized by a terrible misgiving that some form of tragedy would follow his attendance at the meeting. Such fear was hastily overruled by the messengers, whose main concern was to pacify their beleaguered tribesmen. Soon, they had persuaded Hiawatha to follow them and, taking his daughter with him, he pushed his wonderful canoe into the water and set out for the council.

As soon as the people saw him, they sent up shouts of welcome and relief. The venerated warrior climbed ashore and began ascending the steep banks of the lake leading to the place occupied by the council. As he walked, however, he became conscious of a loud, whirring noise overhead. He lifted his eyes upwards and perceived something which looked like a small cloud descending rapidly towards the earth. Filled with terror and alarm, the crowd scattered in confusion, but Hiawatha stood still, instructing his daughter to do the same, for he considered it cowardly to flee, and futile, in any event, to attempt to escape the designs of the Great Spirit. The object approached with greater speed and as it came nearer, it revealed the shape of a gigantic white heron, whose wings, pointed and outstretched, masked all light in the sky. The creature descended with ever-increasing velocity, until, with a mighty crash, it fell upon the girl, instantly crushing her to death.

Hiawatha stared at the spot where the prostrate bird lay and then, in silent anguish, he signalled to a group of warriors nearby to lift the carcass from the earth. They came forward and did as he requested, but when they had moved the bird, not a trace of Hiawatha's daughter was discovered. No word was spoken. The people waited in silence, until at length, Hiawatha stooped to the ground and selected a feather from the snow-white plumage. With this, he decorated his costume, and after he had ensured that other warriors followed his example, he walked in calm dignity to the head of the council.[3] During that first day, he listened gravely and attentively to the different plans of the various tribal chiefs and speakers. But on the second day he arose and with a voice of great authority and strength he began to address his people:

'My friends and brothers, listen to what I say to you. It would be a very foolish thing to challenge these northern invaders in individual tribes. Only by uniting in a common band of brotherhood may we hope to succeed. Let us do this, and we shall swiftly drive the enemy from our land.

'You, the Mohawks, sitting under the shadow of the great tree whose roots sink deep into the earth, you shall be the first nation, because you are warlike and mighty.

'You, the Oneidas, who recline your bodies against the impenetrable stone, you shall be the second nation, because you have never failed to give wise counsel.

'You, the Onondagas, who occupy the land at the foot of the great hills, because you are so gifted in speech, you shall be the third nation.

'You, the Senecas, who reside in the depths of the forest, you shall be the fourth nation, because of your cunning and speed in the hunt.

'And you, the Cayugas, who roam the prairies and possess great wisdom, you shall be the fifth nation, because you understand more than any of us how to raise corn and build lodges.

Opposite: *No one knew exactly where Hiawatha had come from. They knew only that he was of a high and mysterious origin and investigated no further than this.*

'Unite ye five nations, for if we form this powerful alliance, the Great Spirit will smile down on us and we shall remain free, prosperous and happy. But if we remain as we are, always at variance with each other, he will frown upon us and we shall be enslaved or left to perish in the war-storm.

'Brothers, these are the words of Hiawatha. I have said all that I have to say.'

On the following day, Hiawatha's great plan was considered and adopted by the council. Once more, he stood up and addressed the people with wise words of counsel, but even as his speech drew to a close he was being summoned back to the skies by the Great Spirit.

Hiawatha went down to the shore and assumed the seat in his canoe, satisfied within that his mission to the Iroquois had been accomplished. Strange music was heard on the air at that moment and while the wondering multitude stood gazing at their beloved chief, he was silently wafted from sight, and they never saw him again.

1 History would indicate that this was chief Atotarho.
2 The Huron, ancient enemies of the Iroquois, although at one time part of the same race.
3 Since this event, the plumage of the white heron was used by the Onondagas as a decoration while on the war-path.

Ganusquah, Last of the Stone Giants[1]

AS A FINAL DESPERATE MEASURE in the bloody battle to rid themselves of the Stone Giants, the Iroquois called upon the Upholder of the Heavens, Tahahiawagon, to come to their aid. For generations, they had bravely suffered the carnage and destruction alone, but were now so depleted in numbers they agreed they had nowhere else to turn. Tahahiawagon, who had generously provided them with their hunting grounds and fisheries, was already aware of their distress and had waited patiently for the day when he could again demonstrate his loyalty and devotion.

Opposite:
For generations, the people had suffered at the hands of the Stone Giants. Now they turned to Tahahiawagon who had always come to their aid in the past.

Determined to relieve the Iroquois of these merciless invaders, the great god transformed himself into a stone giant and descended to earth where he placed himself among the most influential of their tribes. Before long, the giants began to marvel at his miraculous strength and fearlessness in battle and soon they reached the unanimous decision that Tahahiawagon should act as their new chief. The great god brandished his club high in the air:

'Now we will destroy the Iroquois,' he roared. 'Come, let us make a feast of these puny warriors and invite all the Stone Giants throughout the earth to celebrate it with us.'

Carrying on with his façade, the new chief marched all the Stone Giants towards a strong fort of the Onondagas where he commanded them to lie low in a deep hollow in the valley until sunrise. At dawn, he told them, they would slaughter and destroy all the unsuspecting Indians while they still lay in their beds.

But during the night, Tahahiawagon scaled a great mountain nearby and began hewing the rock-face with an enormous chisel. When he had produced a great mass of boulders he raised his foot and kicked them over the land below. Only one Stone Giant managed to escape the horrifying avalanche. His name was Ganusquah, and he fled as fast as his legs would carry him through the darkness, all the way to the Allegheny Mountains.

As soon as he had reached this spot, he secreted himself in a cave where he remained until he had grown to a huge size and strength. No human being had ever set eyes on him, for to look upon his face meant instant death. He was vulnerable to attack only at the base of his foot, but it was not within the power of any mortal to wound him. And so, Ganusquah used the whole earth as his path, carving out a massive trail through the forests and mountains where his footprints formed huge caverns that filled with water to make the lakes.

If a river obstructed his path, he would swoop it up in his huge hands and turn it from its course. If a mountain stood in his way, he would push his fists through it to create a great tunnel. If ever he were hungry, he would devour a whole herd of buffalo. If ever he were thirsty, he would drink the ocean dry. Even in the tumult of the storms, he made his presence felt, as his voice rose high above the booming of the clouds, warning the Thunderess to keep away from his cave.

It was during one of these terrific storms that Ganusquah came closer than ever before to one of the human species. A young hunter, blinded and bruised by the hail which hurled itself like sharp pebbles upon him, soon lost his trail and took refuge within the hollow of an enormous rock. Nightfall approached, casting deep shadows on the walls of his temporary shelter and soon the young warrior began to drift off to sleep, pleased to have found a place of warmth and safety. He had no sooner indulged this comforting thought, however, when the rock which housed him began to move, but in the queerest manner, almost

Opposite: The young warrior stood up, straining his eyes to find the opening of the cave. But too late, for suddenly he felt a gigantic hand on his shoulder.

as if it was being tilted from side to side with the weight of some vast and heavy burden. The swaying motion intensified and was soon accompanied by the most perplexing jumble of sounds, at one moment as sweet and relaxed as a babbling brook, and the next, as eerie and tormented as a death-cry.

The young warrior stood up in alarm, straining his eyes to find the opening of the cave. But too late, for suddenly he felt a gigantic hand on his shoulder and heard a loud voice rumbling in his ear:

'Young warrior, beware! You are in the cave of the stone giant, Ganusquah. Close your eyes and do not look at me, for no human has yet survived who has gazed upon my face. Many have wandered into this cave, but they have come to hunt me. You alone have come here for shelter and I will not, therefore, turn you away.

'I shall spare your life if you agree to obey my commands for as long as I consider necessary. Although I will remain unseen, you will hear my voice whenever I wish to speak to you, and I will always be there to help you as you roam the earth. From here you must go forth and live freely among the animals, the birds and the fish. All these are your ancestors and it will be your task hereafter to dedicate your life to them.

'You will encounter many of them along your way. Do not pass until you have felled a strong tree and carved their image in the wood grain. When you first strike a tree, if it speaks, know that it is my voice urging you on with your task. Each tree has a voice and you must learn the language of the entire forest.

'Now, go on your way. I will be watching you and guiding you. Teach mankind kindness, the unspoken kindness of nature, and so win your way in life forever.'

The young hunter walked out into the darkness and when he awoke next morning he found himself seated at the base of a basswood tree which gradually transformed itself into a mask and began relating to him the great breadth of its power.

The mask was the supreme being of the forest. It could see behind the stars. It could conjure up storms and summon the sunshine. It knew the remedy for each disease and could overpower death. The venomous reptiles knew its threat and avoided its path. It knew every poisonous root and could repel their evil influence.

'I am Gogonsa,' said the mask. 'My tree is basswood and there is nothing like it in the forest. My wood is soft and will make your task easier. My timber is porous and the sunlight can enter its

Opposite:
'Now, go on your way,' Ganusquah, the Stone Giant, told him. 'Teach mankind the unspoken kindness of nature. I will be watching and guiding you always.'

darkness. Even the wind can whisper to it and it will hear. Ganusquah has called upon me to help you and when he is satisfied with your work, I will lead you back to your people.'

The young hunter listened carefully to every word of advice Gogonsa offered him and then, forearmed with this knowledge, he set about the task of carving the gogonsasooh, the 'false faces' of the forest. On his travels he met many curious animals, birds, reptiles and insects, which he detained until he had carved them in the basswood, inviting them to stay with him until he had learned their language and customs. Guided by the voice of Ganusquah, he moved deeper into the forest and soon he had learned to interpret its many different voices, including the voices of the trees and grasses, mosses and flowers. He learned to love his surroundings and every last creature he encountered, and he knew he would be loathe to leave this world of his ancestors when the time eventually came for him to return to his own home.

A great many years were passed in this way until the hunter, who had entered the cave as a youth, had become an old man, bent in two with the burden of the gogonsasooh he carried with him from place to place. At last, he heard the voice of Ganusquah pronouncing an end to his labour and soon the mask appeared to guide him back to his own people. He wondered if he had the strength to make the journey, but he refused to abandon what he now considered his most precious possessions, the hundreds of gogonsasooh he had carved in basswood.

Wearily, he set off on the track, almost crushed by his heavy load, but after only a short time, he felt a sudden surge of energy. Slowly, his spine began to uncurl, his back began to broaden and strengthen and he felt himself growing taller until he had become a giant in stature, rising high above the trees. He stood up tall and proud and smiled, unaware that in the distance, a great cave had begun to crumble.

1 Please refer to the glossary for background detail on the Stone Giants.

Great Head and the Ten Brothers

Opposite:
It was agreed among the remaining family that the eldest boy should go out shortly after sunrise on the following morning in search of his brothers.

IN A REMOTE INDIAN VILLAGE at the edge of the forest, an orphaned family of ten boys lived in a small lodge with their uncle. The five elder brothers went out to hunt every day, but the younger ones, not yet ready for so rigorous a life, remained at home with their uncle,

never daring to venture too far from their home.

One day, the group of elder brothers, who had been away deer-hunting, failed to return at the usual hour. As the evening wore on, there was still no sign of them, and by nightfall their uncle had become extremely worried for their safety. It was agreed among the remaining family that the eldest boy should go out on the following morning in search of his brothers. He readily accepted the challenge and he set off after sunrise, confident that he would locate them before long. But the boy did not return, and his disappearance caused even greater consternation among the household.

'We must find out what is happening to them,' said the next in line. 'Though I am young and ill-prepared for adventure, I cannot bear to picture any of my family lying wounded in some fearful, hostile place.'

And so, having obtained his uncle's permission, he too set off enthusiastically, though he was not so self-assured as his brother before him. Just like the others, however, the youth failed to reappear, and an identical fate awaited the two more after him who took it upon themselves to go out in search of the lost hunters. At length, only one small brother remained with his uncle at the lodge, and fearing he might lose the last of his young nephews, the old man became very protective of him, turning a deaf ear to his persistent pleas to be allowed to take his turn in the search.

The youngest brother was now obliged to accompany his uncle everywhere. He was even forced to walk with the old man the short distance to the wood-pile, and he longed for the day when adventure would come knocking on his door. He had almost resigned himself to the fact that this would never happen when, one morning, as the pair stooped to gather firewood, the young boy imagined he heard a deep groan coming from the earth beneath his feet. He called upon his uncle to listen and the sound, unmistakably a human groan, soon repeated itself. Both were deeply shocked by the discovery and began clawing frantically at the earth with their bare hands. Shortly afterwards, a human face revealed itself and before long, they had uncovered the entire body of a man, caked in mould and scarcely able to breathe.

Carefully, they lifted the unfortunate creature from the soil and carried him into their lodge where they rubbed his skin down with bear oil until he slowly began to revive. It was several hours before the man could bring himself to speak, but then, at last, he began mouthing a few words, informing his hosts that he had been out hunting when his mind had suddenly become entirely blank. He could remember nothing more, he told them, neither his name, nor the village he had come from. The old man and his nephew begged the stranger to stay with them, hoping that soon his memory would be restored and that then, perhaps, he could help them in their own search.

The days passed by, but after only a very short time, the young boy and his uncle began to observe that the person they had rescued was no ordinary mortal like themselves. He did not eat any of the food they served him, but his strength increased daily none the less. He had no need of sleep, and often when it rained he behaved very strangely, tossing restlessly in his chair and calling aloud in a curious language.

One night, a particularly violent storm raged outside. As the rain pelted down and the winds howled fiercely, the boy and his uncle were awoken by the loud cries of their guest:

'Do you hear that noise?' he yelled. 'That is my brother, Great Head, riding on the wind. Can you not hear him wailing?'

'Yes, we can,' said the old man. 'Would you like us to invite him here? Would he come if you sent for him?'

'I would certainly like to see him,' replied the strange guest, 'but he will not come unless I bring him here by magic. You should prepare for him a welcoming meal, ten large blocks of maple-wood, for that is the food he lives on.' And saying this, the stranger departed in search of his brother, taking with him his bow and a selection of arrows, carved from the roots of a hickory-tree.

At about midday, he drew near to Great Head's dwelling and quickly transformed himself into a mole, so that his brother would not notice his approach. Silently, he crept through the grass until he spotted Great Head up ahead, perched on a cliff-face, glowering fiercely at an owl.

'I see you!' shouted Great Head, 'now you shall die.' And he lunged forward, ready to devour the helpless creature.

Just at that moment, the mole stood up, and taking aim with his bow, shot an arrow in Great Head's direction. The arrow became larger and larger as it sped through the air towards the monstrous creature, but then, when it had almost reached its target, it turned back on itself and returned to the mole, regaining its normal size. Great Head was soon in pursuit, puffing and snorting like a hurricane as he trampled through the trees. Once more, the mole shot an arrow and again it returned to him, luring Great Head further and further onwards towards the lodge where the young boy and his uncle nervously awaited their arrival.

As soon as the door to their house burst open, its terrified occupants began attacking Great Head with wooden mallets. But the more vigorously they struck him, the more Great Head broke into peals of laughter, for he was not only impervious to pain, but the sight of his brother standing before him had put him in the best of moods. The two embraced warmly and Great Head sat down to his meal of maple-blocks which he devoured with great relish.

When he had done, he thanked his hosts for their hospitality and enquired of them how he might return their kindness. They began telling him the story of their missing relatives, but had only uttered a few words before Great Head interrupted them:

'You need tell me no more,' he said to them, 'I know precisely what has become of them. They have fallen into the hands of a woodland witch. Now if this boy will accompany me, I will point out her dwelling and show him the bones of his brothers.'

Although reluctant to release him, the uncle perceived how anxious his nephew was to learn the fate of his brothers. Finally, he gave his consent, and the young boy started off with Great Head, smiling broadly at the thought of the adventure which lay ahead.

They did not once pause for rest and after a time they came upon a ramshackle hut, in front of which were strewn dry bones of every size and description. In the doorway sat a crooked old witch, rocking back and forth, singing to herself. When she looked up and saw her visitors, she flew into a rage and began chanting her spell to change the living into dry bones. But her magic had no effect on Great Head, and because his companion stood in his shadow, he too was protected from the charm. The youth sprang forward and began to attack the frail, old witch, beating her with his fists until she fell lifeless to the ground. As soon as she lay dead, a loud shriek pierced the silence, and her flesh was transformed into black-feathered birds that rose squawking into the air.

The young boy now set about the task of selecting the bones of his brothers. It was slow and difficult work, but, at last, he had gathered together nine white mounds. Great Head came forward to examine each of them and when he was satisfied that no bone was missing he spoke to his young companion:

Opposite: Finally, his uncle gave his consent and the young boy set off on his journey with Great Head, smiling broadly at the thought of the adventure which lay ahead.

'I am going back to my rock,' he told him. 'But do not despair or think I have abandoned you, for soon you will see me again.'

The boy stood alone, guarding the heaps of bones, trying to decide whether he should make his way back home before daylight faded. Looking upwards, he noticed that a huge storm was gathering and began walking towards the hut for shelter. The hail beat on his back even as he walked the short distance and soon sharp needles of rain pricked his skin all over. The thunder now clashed and lightning struck the ground wherever he attempted to step. The young boy grew fearful and flung himself to the earth, but suddenly he heard a familiar voice calling to him, and lifting his eyes, he saw Great Head riding at the centre of the storm.

'Arise you bones,' Great Head yelled, 'I bid you come to life.' The hurricane passed overhead in an instant, as rapidly as it had first appeared. The young boy felt certain that he must have been dreaming, but then, he observed that the mounds had disappeared. In a moment he was surrounded by his brothers and huge tears of relief and joy flooded down his cheeks.

Sayadio and the Magic Cup[1]

MANY MONTHS HAD PASSED since the young brave, Sayadio, lost his beautiful young sister to a fatal illness. She had been only twelve years old when she died, and her abrupt departure to the Land of Souls had left a deep sadness in the hearts of all who had known her. Sayadio occupied himself as best he could after her death and attempted to carry on a normal life, but often he could not prevent himself falling into the blackest of moods from which it took several long weeks to rouse himself.

Worried that his grief would never be silenced, he decided the time had come to call upon his manitto[2] for help. He found a place of solitude and meditated hard, and soon he heard a voice calling to him:

'Your mourning will only cease', it told him, 'when you have followed the path your sister has taken to the Land of Souls.' Sayadio welcomed the advice of his manitto and in great haste he began making preparations for his journey, resolving to be reunited with his sister before long and to bring her back with him on his return.

Opposite: It was not long before Sayadio approached the Land of Souls and, filled with excitement, he began to call his sister's name over and over again.

But the path ahead was never-ending and the months crept by without offering any sign of improvement. Sayadio began to despair and was just about ready to abandon his quest when, quite unexpectedly, he encountered a stooped old man moving slowly towards him along the same track. The stranger's great white beard

trailed the ground and in his right hand he carried a heavy, silver object which, on closer inspection, proved to be a curious type of drinking vessel.

'Can I help you on your way,' Sayadio offered, 'perhaps I can carry something for you.'

'I need go no further,' replied the old man, 'for I have set out to meet you so that I might give you this gourd. If ever you find your sister, use the gourd to catch her spirit and hold it captive until you have returned to your earthly home.'

Delighted to receive such a valuable gift, Sayadio travelled onwards, his mood brighter than it had been for many weeks. It was not long before he approached the outskirts of the Land of Souls and, filled with excitement, he began to call his sister's name over and over again. He received no answer, but he did not feel dejected, for up ahead, in the distance, he suddenly noticed a group of spirits playing in the meadow. Respectfully he advanced towards them, expecting that they would greet him kindly, but to his utter dismay, the spirits fled in horror as soon as they set eyes on him.

At that particular time of year, according to ancient custom, the dead were due to gather together for a great dance ceremony presided over by the Holder of the Heavens, Tarenyawago. Soon the spirit-drum began to beat loudly and the sound of an Indian flute filled the air. The effect of these instruments was almost instantaneous, for the spirits immediately abandoned their hiding places and thronged into a circle anxious to commence their bewildering ritual. Sayadio peered from behind the trees and quickly spotted his sister among the spirits. Without warning, he sprang forward, uncorked his gourd, and attempted to sweep her into the vessel. But she eluded his grasp without any trouble and dissolved into thin air before he knew quite what had happened.

Defeated and despondent, Sayadio made a desperate appeal to the Holder of the Heavens:

'I have come a very long way', he informed the great and powerful spirit, 'because my sister was taken from us before her time. Please will you help me to capture her soul, so that she may be returned to her earthly home and to those who love her.'

Observing the deep perplexity and sadness of the young man, Tarenyawago took pity on him and kindly offered his assistance.

'Take this magic rattle', he told Sayadio, 'and shake it as soon as you catch sight of the spirits gathering again to complete their dance.

Be patient, yet swift, and you will succeed in your ambition.'

Shortly before sunset, just as the Holder of the Heavens had promised, the spirits began floating on the air like a thick mist, descending one by one on exactly the same spot as before. Once more, Sayadio saw his sister among the group, stepping lightly, round and round, to the sound of the eerie melody. She appeared to be wholly entranced by the music, and he took this opportunity to step forward cautiously with his magic rattle. As soon as she passed before him again, he shook it delicately in her ear and this time, to his great relief, he found that she came to an abrupt halt, frozen in motion like a graceful statue. Quick as a flash, he swooped her off the ground and into his gourd, securely fastening the lid and ignoring the pitiful cries of the captured soul struggling to regain its liberty.

Retracing his steps homeward, Sayadio soon reached his native village where he summoned his friends and relatives to come and examine the strange gourd housing his precious charge. He called for the body of his sister to be brought forth from its burial-place, for he intended, without further delay, to enact the ceremony that would reunite her spirit with her body. Everything was almost ready for the sacred rite of resurrection when, out of nowhere, the most witless Indian in the village rushed forward and removed the lid of the gourd, no longer able to control his immoderate curiosity.

Without any hesitation, the imprisoned spirit rose up into the air, and failing to look back, glided high up into the sky, disappearing over the horizon. Sayadio gazed helplessly in the direction of its frantic flight, calling upon the departed spirit to return to him, but it made no response to his plea. Overwhelmed with despair, he retreated to his lodge, but soon he heard the familiar voice of his manitto whispering in his ear:

'The spirit of your sister was not destined for this mortal world,' the voice explained. 'She is happy in her new home, so be at peace and cease your mourning.'

Sayadio listened and his grief suddenly abandoned him. And from that day forth, he never again attempted to recall his sister from the dead.

1 A legend from the Wyandot tribe of the Iroquois

2. Please see glossary note

※   ※   ※

MYTHS OF
THE ALGONQUIAN PEOPLE

HE ALGONQUIAN RACE[1] was one of the largest of the North American Indians, comprising well over a hundred different tribes. From east to west their territory spread from the Atlantic coast as far as the base of the Rocky Mountains and from north to south it extended above the St Lawrence Valley all the way southwards into Illinois and Virginia. The most famous tribes of the Algonquian family included the Blackfeet, Cheyenne and Arapapho in the west; the Abnaki, Delawares, Shawnees, Powhattans and Mohicans in the east; the Chippewas, Crees, Montagnais and Micmacs in the north and north-east, and the Menominees and Kickapoos in the central and southern regions.

The Algonquin Indians were a tall, well-proportioned race, intelligent and obliging, who worked the land or hunted and fished for their survival. Those belonging to the eastern tribes living along the Atlantic were the first native Americans to come into contact with the white settlers. They welcomed the white man and passed on to him the domestic skills they had acquired, even yielding to him many of their most fertile coastal lands. Ultimately, the Algonquins were driven further and further westwards by the settlers, coming into headlong conflict with their old enemies, the Iroquois, and losing almost all of their original territories.

Algonquian myths and legends are some of the most colourful of all native American mythology. A selection of the more well-known tales, introducing the most popular heroic figures, cultural practices, beliefs and general lifestyle of the Algonquin Indians are retold here.

1 The term 'Algonquian' is used to describe the whole linguistic stock, for example, we would speak of the 'Algonquian race', whereas the term 'Algonquin' is the adjective applied to individuals within this linguistic grouping, e.g., 'Algonquin Indians'.

The Great Deeds of Michabo

A VERY POWERFUL MANITTO once visited the earth and, falling in love with its only inhabitant, a beautiful young maiden, he made her his wife. From this union were born four healthy sons, but in giving birth the mother sadly passed away. The first son was named Michabo[1] and he was destined to become the friend of the human race. The second, Chibiabos, took charge of the dead and ruled the Land of Souls. The third, Wabassa, immediately fled to the north, transforming himself into a rabbit-spirit, while the fourth, Chokanipok, who was of a fiery temperament, spent his time arguing, especially with his eldest brother.

Michabo, the strongest and most courageous of the four, had always attributed the death of his mother to Chokanipok, and the repeated combats between the two were often fiercely savage. During one particularly brutal confrontation, Michabo carved huge fragments of flesh from the body of his brother which, as soon as they fell to the ground, were transformed into flintstones. In time, the children of men found a use for these stones and used them to create fire, giving Chokanipok the name of Firestone, or Man of Flint.

After a long and tortuous battle, Chokanipok was finally slain by Michabo who tore out his bowels and changed them into long twining vines from which the earth's vegetation sprung forth. After this, Michabo journeyed far and wide, carrying with him all manner of tools and equipment which he distributed among men. He gave them lances and arrow-points; he taught them how to make axes or agukwats; he devised the art of knitting nets to catch fish; he furnished the hunter with charms and signs to use in his chase, and he taught mankind to lay traps and snares. In the course of his journeys he also killed the ferocious beasts and monsters threatening the human race and cleared the rivers and streams of many of the obstructions which the Evil Spirit had placed there.

When he saw that all this was done, Michabo placed four good spirits at the four cardinal points of the earth, instructing mankind that he should always blow the smoke from his calumet in each of these four directions as a mark of respect during the sacred feasts. The Spirit of the North, he told them, would always provide snow and ice, enabling man to hunt game. The Spirit of the South would give them melons, maize and tobacco. The Spirit he had placed in the West would ensure that rain fell upon the crops, and the Spirit of the East would never fail to bring light in place of darkness.

Opposite: Algonquin Indians were a tall, well-proportioned race, intelligent and obliging, who worked the land or hunted and fished for their survival.

Then, retreating to an immense slab of ice in the Northern Ocean, Michabo kept a watchful eye on mankind, informing them that if ever the day should arrive when their wickedness forced him to depart the earth, his footprints would catch fire and the end of the world would come; for it was he who directed the sun in his daily walks around the earth.

1 Michabo, supreme deity of the Algonquin Indians, is very often represented as an invincible god, endowed with marvellous powers. Sometimes, however, he is given a far more human treatment, and is depicted as a trickster, or troublemaker, as in the story to follow.

Michabo Defeats the King of Fishes

ONE MORNING, MICHABO went out upon the lake in his canoe to fish. Casting his line into the middle of the water, he began to shout: 'Meshenahmahgwai, King of Fishes, grab hold of my bait, you cannot escape me forever.'

For a full hour he continued to call out these words until, at last, the King of Fishes, who had been attempting to rest at the bottom of the lake, could bear the dreadful commotion no longer.

'Michabo is beginning to irritate me,' he complained. 'Here, trout, take hold of the bait and keep this fellow silent.'

The trout obeyed the request and sunk its jaws into the hook as Michabo commenced drawing in his catch. The line, which was very heavy, caused his canoe to stand almost perpendicular in the water, but he persevered bravely until the fish appeared above the surface. As soon as he saw the trout, however, he began to roar angrily: 'Esa, Esa! Shame! Shame! Why did you take hold of my hook, you ugly creature?'

The trout let go at once and swam back down to the bottom of the lake. Michabo then cast his line into the water once more saying: 'King of Fishes, I am still waiting and I will remain here for as long as it takes.'

This time the King of Fishes caught hold of a giant sunfish and commanded him to do exactly as the trout had done before him. The sunfish obeyed and Michabo again drew up his line, his canoe turning in swift circles with the weight of the monstrous creature. Michabo felt certain he had succeeded and began crying out in excitement:

'Wha-wee-he! Wha-wee-he!' But he was quickly made to realize that he had been deceived once more and his face turned a bright shade of crimson as he screamed into the water:

'Esa! Esa! You hideous fish. You have contaminated my hook by placing it in your big mouth. Let go of it, you filthy brute.' The sunfish dropped the hook and disappeared below the surface of the lake.

'Meshenahmahgwai! I have reached the end of my patience,' Michabo bellowed with increasing fury. 'Do as I have bid you and take hold of my hook.'

By now, the King of Fishes was himself seething with anger and he grabbed hold of the bait, allowing himself to be tugged upwards through the water. He had no sooner reached the surface, however, when he opened his mouth wide, and in one gulp, swallowed Michabo, his fishing rod and his little wooden canoe.

Michabo stumbled about in the belly of the fish wondering, for an instant, who had turned the lights out in the sky. But then, he felt a sudden motion and a tremendous rumbling noise and it dawned on him that the King of Fishes had helped himself to an early supper. Michabo glanced around him and seeing his war-club lying in his canoe, lifted it above his shoulders and brought it down mercilessly wherever he could find a solid wall. He was hurled to and fro as the King of Fishes responded to these blows and complained to those around him:

'I am sick in my stomach for having swallowed that troublemaker, Michabo. He has not provided a satisfying meal.' And as he spoke, Michabo continued with his attack, delivering a number of very severe blows to the fish's heart.

The King of Fishes began to heave violently and, fearing that he would be thrown up into the lake to drown, Michabo quickly rammed his canoe lengthways into the fish's throat. The pain induced by the obstruction, combined with the repeated beating he suffered internally, caused the King's heart to stop beating, and soon his great body, battered and lifeless, was tossed up by the waves upon the shore.

Michabo sat down in the darkness, faced now with an even greater problem, for he had not paused to consider how he would manage to free himself from the bowels of the King of Fishes once his victim lay dead. Had he been ejected, he might have stood some small chance of survival in spite of the fact that he could not swim, but now, there seemed little or no hope.

He chastized himself for his own folly and had begun to come to terms with his sorry fate when, all of a sudden, his ears were filled with the sound of tapping noises above his head. Certain that the King of Fishes lay dead, he was puzzled by the rhythm, but its source was soon revealed to him, as light began to filter in through an opening in the fleshy roof and the heads of gulls peered into the darkness below.

'What a good thing that you have come, my friends,' cried

Michabo. 'Quickly, make the opening larger so that I can get out.' The birds, utterly astonished to discover Michabo in the belly of a fish, chattered excitedly as they obeyed the god's command. In no time at all Michabo found himself at liberty and smiled broadly to find his feet touching firm soil once more.

'I have been foolish,' he told the gulls, 'and you have shown great kindness in releasing me from my confinement. From this day forth, you shall not be looked upon as scavengers, but shall be known as Kayosk, Noble Scratchers, and receive my special blessing.'

Then, walking towards the shores of the lake, Michabo breathed life into the King of Fishes, restoring him to his former glory. The King took up his usual place at the bottom of the water and in this silent world, undisturbed by the cries of a keen fisherman, he carried on with his rest.

The Land of Souls

THE WEDDING CEREMONY OF A HANDSOME, young Algonquin chief was fast approaching. He had chosen for his bride a very beautiful woman from a neighbouring tribe. The two had fallen deeply in love and looked forward to a long and happy life together, but sadly this was not to be, for on the eve of their wedding the young woman succumbed to a raging fever and within hours she had passed away, leaving her intended husband grief-stricken and distraught.

The handsome chief, who had once been famous for his courage and heroism throughout the land, now spent all of his time in mourning, making a daily pilgrimage to the burial place of his beloved where he threw himself on the soft mound and sobbed helplessly. Hunting and warfare no longer held any charm for him and he cast aside his bow and arrow, resolving never to use his weapon again. The situation appeared hopeless and even the chief's closest friends began to believe that he would never mend his broken heart or recover his brave reputation.

One day, however, the chief overheard a conversation among the elders of his tribe which, for the first time in many months, prompted him to join the circle and listen attentively. The old men were discussing their loved ones who had died, and they also spoke of a path leading to the spirit-world which, if a man was lucky enough to find it, enabled the living to visit the dead. The grieving young lover

Opposite: The King of Fishes had no sooner reached the surface when he opened his mouth wide, and in one gulp, swallowed Michabo and his little wooden canoe.

eagerly welcomed this unexpected news and, taking up his weapon and a few meagre belongings, set off immediately to discover the path that would lead him to the Land of Souls.

He had no firm idea which direction he should take, but instinct informed him that he must keep travelling southward until he observed some change in the landscape. His journey over the snow-covered fields and hills was both difficult and wearisome, but after fourteen days, he became convinced of a difference in the appearance of the surrounding countryside. Certainly, the thick snow had begun to melt. The sky, too, was of a more radiant blue and the trees had begun to reveal tiny leaf-buds. Moving onwards, as if by enchantment, delicate and colourful flowers emerged from the soil, birds began to chirp sweet melodies and the air grew warm and fragrant. The young chief's heart began to beat with excitement at these changes, for he knew that he must be nearing the Land of Souls.

A rugged path wound its way through the trees of the spreading forest before him and he felt sure that he must follow this path. Passing through a dark grove, he came upon a little lodge set high up on a hill. In the doorway stood an old man, his hair as white as snow and his eyes as bright as sapphires. He wore a robe of swan-skin and in his right hand he carried a long staff with which he beckoned the young chief forward.

'I have been expecting you,' said the old man. 'Come inside the lodge and I will answer all the questions I know you wish to ask me.'

There was no need for the chief to inform the stranger of his quest, since the old man already knew every detail of his misfortune.

'Only a few days ago the beautiful woman you seek rested here within my lodge,' he said to the chief. 'Now she has gone to the Land of Souls and you can follow her there if you do as I say and listen carefully to my counsel.'

'You cannot take your body along with you, nor will your bow and arrow be of any use,' the old man told him. 'Leave them here and they will be returned to you when we meet again. I must warn you that the journey ahead is a perilous one. You now stand at the border of the Land of Souls and you must cross that vast lake beyond to reach the Island of the Blessed where it will be possible for you to visit your loved one again.'

The young chief, who was in no way frightened by the old man's words of caution, grew impatient to be on his way once more. He found, as he travelled onwards, that the forests, rivers and mountains had taken on an almost ethereal quality. Animals bounded along gleefully by his side and as he moved swiftly through thickets and dense woodlands, he realized that he was now a weightless spirit floating effortlessly and fearlessly through the air in the Land of Souls.

It was not long before he reached the broad lake the old man had described to him. Gazing across its waters, he caught sight of a very beautiful island shimmering in the midday sunshine. A canoe of white, shining stone lay tied upon the shore, and the young chief lost no time jumping aboard it and grasping the paddles. He was just about to pull away in the direction of the island when he was struck by a powerful sense that he was no longer alone on the water. Turning to confront his mysterious companion, he was utterly amazed and delighted to see his young bride seated in an identical canoe alongside him, ready to accompany him on his crossing to the Island of the Blessed.

At first, the surface of the silver lake remained as smooth as glass, disturbed only by tiny ripples of frolicking trout anxious to join in the excursion. But then, as the couple approached the half-way mark, the waves of the lake began to swell dramatically in strength and size. The water now changed to a steely-grey colour and as the young chief peered over the side of his canoe, he was shocked to discover several human skulls floating on the spray. He remembered the old man's words, that it would be a hazardous journey, and thought now of those who had attempted it before him, battling on bravely, yet eventually drowning in the furious tempest.

Though he was filled with terror and fear for the safety of both himself and his bride, the young chief did not alter his course but continued to row boldly towards the shore, never once losing sight of his loved one. The Master of Life kept a watchful eye on them from above and, knowing that they were innocent children whose deeds in life had been free of evil, he decreed that they should reach the island unharmed. Suddenly the winds began to ease, the water grew calm and the young couple at last felt their canoes grating on the golden sand.

Leaping on to the island, they embraced each other rapturously, shedding many tears of relief and joy. Then, as they stood hand in hand, they surveyed the perfect world they now occupied where everything seemed designed to bring them the utmost pleasure. The air itself was like an exquisite, mouth-watering food sent to nourish and strengthen them. Walking through the beautiful countryside, they could find no trace of suffering or sadness, no cold or discomfort, no war or destruction, only the sights and sounds of a perfect paradise of nature.

For three days and three nights, the young lovers remained free to enjoy this blissful land, each of them hoping that their happiness would last forever. But on the third evening, the young chief was awoken by a gentle voice calling to him on the breeze:

'Your time has not yet come,' whispered the Master of Life. 'You must return to your own people and fulfil your mortal destiny. Rule them wisely and well, for they need your guidance at this time, and when you have completed your duty to them, you may return here and join forever the bride you must now abandon.'

The young chief rose obediently and, making his way to the old man's lodge on the far side of the lake, re-entered the body he had left behind. Although he was heavy-hearted, he was not resentful of his departure, but felt honoured that the Master of Life had intervened to set him on the correct path.

Returning to his people, the young chief became a just and kindly ruler, winning the admiration and loyalty of all who knew him. Often, at the end of a long hunt, he would call for a great fire to be built and ordering his people to sit around it, he would tell them of the Land of Souls and describe to them the path he knew he would follow once more as soon as he had served his time as father to his people.

The Gift of Corn

But the place was not forgotten
Where he wrestled with Mondamin;
Nor forgotten nor neglected
Was the grave where lay Mondamin,
Sleeping in the rain and sunshine,
Where his scattered plumes and garments
Faded in the rain and sunshine. [1]

LONG AGO, THERE LIVED A POOR INDIAN who dwelt with his wife and children in a tiny lodge in the heart of the forest. The family relied on hunting for their food, and although the father was never lacking in courage and skill, there were often times when he returned home without provisions, so that his wife and children had only the leaves on the trees to satisfy their hunger. The eldest son of the family, a boy of fourteen, had inherited the same kind and gentle disposition as his

Opposite: As he roamed the fields and mountains, the boy was deeply moved by the beauty of his surroundings, the glorious flowers, the succulent berries.

father, and as he watched the old man struggle to take care of them all, he longed only for the time when he would be able to help out in some way.

At last, the young boy reached the age of the great fast, when he was obliged to shut himself away without food, praying night and day to the Great Spirit in preparation for the coming of his spirit-guide and guardian through life. This solemn and sacred event demanded that he empty his mind and heart of every evil thought and he now began to meditate earnestly on the generosity of the Great Spirit who never ceased to provide mankind with everything good and wholesome. As he roamed the fields and mountains during the first few days of his retreat, he was deeply moved by the beauty of his surroundings, the glorious flowers, the succulent berries, and he felt the strong desire to make his own contribution to this remarkable world.

The young boy was well aware that both he and his family were deeply indebted to the Great Spirit, but at the same time, he began asking himself why it was that the divine ruler had not made it easier for them to find enough food to survive on.

'Perhaps if I pray very hard,' the boy thought to himself, 'the Great Spirit will reveal to me in a dream the means by which I can ease the hardship my family now suffers.' And with that he lay down and kept to his bed for a full day and a night.

It was now the fifth day of his fast and the boy lay feeble with hunger, drifting in and out of sleep and hoping that some sort of vision would soon come to him. Suddenly the room in which he lay became filled with a dazzling light, out of which emerged a beautiful young man who moved gracefully towards him. The stranger's slender form was draped in a luxurious, satin robe of green and yellow, his complexion was the purest marble-white and on his head he wore an exotic plume of jade-green feathers. The boy was startled by the apparition, but the stranger's eyes conveyed the gentlest, warmest expression and his voice was as sweet as music as he spoke.

'The Great Spirit has been listening to your prayers,' he said softly. 'He understands how deeply you care for your family and he knows that you have always been a loyal and obedient child. For these reasons he has sent me to guide you in your pursuit and to ensure that your desire is fulfilled.'

Opposite: At last, the boy reached the age of the great fast, when he was obliged to shut himself away without food, praying night and day to the Great Spirit.

'Arise young warrior,' added the beautiful stranger, 'and prepare yourself to wrestle with me, for such is the wish of the Great Spirit.'

Even though his limbs were weak from fasting, the young boy stood up courageously and did as the stranger commanded him. The struggle which followed was long and punishing and at length the boy began to grow faint. But just at this precise moment, the stranger called a halt to the conflict, promising to return on the following day when the boy had replenished his strength.

At exactly the same hour next morning, the celestial visitor reappeared and the two took up the fighting once more. As they battled on, the young boy felt his strength improve and his courage increase. He threw himself wholeheartedly into the struggle, wrestling fiercely with his visitor, until the latter was forced to cry out in pain.

'You have certainly proven your worth today,' the stranger declared, 'now it is my turn to rest before we begin our final trial. Tomorrow will be the seventh day of your fast,' he continued, 'and your father will bring you food to strengthen you. In the evening, you will wrestle with me and easily overcome me, for you have succeeded in winning the favour of the Great Spirit.

'As soon as I have fallen, you must strip me of my garments and bury me in the earth. Once a month, come and cover me with fresh soil and make certain that no weeds or grass are allowed to grow upon my grave. If you do all this, I shall return to life and I promise that you will see me again, splendidly clothed in a garment of green.'

The stranger had no sooner spoken these words than he vanished into thin air, leaving his opponent to fathom the meaning of all that he had been told.

Shortly after dawn on the following day, the young boy's father filled a small basket with nourishing food and set off in search of his son. He was greatly relieved to see the boy again, but noticed that he had grown thin and frail.

'My son, you must eat something,' he urged him. 'You have fasted long enough and I feel certain that the Great Spirit does not require you to sacrifice your own life.'

'Father,' the boy replied, 'please be patient with me until sundown, and at that hour I will happily partake of the meal you have brought me.'

For the young boy was determined to prove his hero's strength without assistance, resolving to rely on his inner strength alone during the trial ahead.

Once again, at the usual hour, the stranger appeared and the contest was renewed as before. Though he had not eaten any of his father's food, or allowed even a drop of water to pass his lips, the boy felt invigorated and irrepressible. Fired by the need to achieve some great purpose, he lunged at his handsome opponent, pushing him violently against a rock in the ground. The stranger did not rise up again to challenge him and, as he bent over to examine him where he lay, the boy could find no trace of life in the handsome youth. A deep sadness and regret suddenly invaded his soul as he began digging the earth to bury the body and he swore to himself that he would tend the grave as lovingly as if it were that of his own mother.

Throughout the spring which followed, the boy never once allowed a day to slip past without visiting the burial place of his friend. He stooped and carefully weeded out the grass and carried fresh soil up the mountain to replace the old, just as he had vowed he would. By summertime, tiny green shoots began to appear in the earth, but because they so reminded the young boy of the feather plume his visitor always wore, he was loathe to remove them and so they continued to rise in height as the months progressed.

The days and weeks passed by and during all of this time, the boy never once revealed to a single soul the purpose of his regular excursions up into the mountains. Then one day, he gingerly approached his father requesting that he follow him on his mysterious ramble. Though he was surprised and a little apprehensive, the old man agreed to accompany his son and soon they had reached the spot where the handsome stranger lay buried.

The sight which now greeted them was truly the most astonishing and gratifying they had ever witnessed. Overnight, the green shoots on the grave had broadened out into beautiful, graceful plants with velvet-soft foliage, each one bearing a generous golden cluster crowned by a majestic plume.

Leaping for joy, the young boy began shouting aloud: 'It is my friend, the friend of my vision who promised he would return to me.'

'It is Mondamin,'² replied his father, filled with admiration for his son. 'It is the spirit grain the old ones have sometimes spoken of, the Indian corn which the Merciful Master has sent to nourish us because he is greatly pleased with you.'

And the two began to gather the golden ears of corn, tearing away the green husks from the stalks as once the young boy had torn away the garments of his extraordinary wrestling companion.

From that day forward, the people no longer depended entirely on hunting and were blessed with beautiful fields of healthy grain which they harvested every year just as soon as the long hot summer had begun to fade into autumn.

1 These lines are taken from Longfellow's narrative poem, 'The Song of Hiawatha,' which incorporates this old Algonquin legend.

2 From the words moedo, meaning 'spirit' and min, meaning 'grain' or 'berry'.

Moowis, the Snow-husband

IN A NORTHERN VILLAGE of the Algonquin tribe there lived a young maiden whose exquisite beauty had won her great fame throughout the region. Every day a whole host of admirers made their way to her father's lodge hoping for an opportunity to feast their eyes on the beautiful young woman. The path to his door was now so well worn, the old man had often considered sending his daughter away but, at the same time, he was fiercely proud of his child and was certain that one day a deserving young warrior would appear and carry her off as his bride.

The young maiden was not so easily satisfied, however, and as the months passed by, she became more and more conscious of her charms, treating her suitors as mere playthings no matter how sincere their intentions towards her. One noble brave, in particular, greatly desired to take the young maiden for his wife. He was of a very kind and sensitive nature, and it was many weeks before he managed to pluck up the courage to visit her at her father's lodge. Kneeling before the beautiful girl, he poured forth from the depths of his soul every agonizing detail of his passion, revealing that he could no longer sleep for love of her, nor partake of any activity without heaviness in his heart. But the young maiden laughed aloud to hear all of this and, failing to consider the appalling cruelty of her response, called to a group of friends nearby and carried on loudly mocking her rejected lover.

By sundown, the entire village had been informed of the morning's events and the noble brave was forced to retire to the solitude of his lodge, overwhelmed by feelings of shame and humiliation. A deep melancholy invaded his spirit and for days on end he remained seated in a fixed position, staring blankly at the walls and refusing to eat, drink or speak. Even when his family and friends began making preparations for the annual migration to their summer camp, he

Opposite: The young maiden's beauty had won her great fame. The path to her door was well worn by a host of admirers hoping to catch even a glimpse of her.

refused to join them, but took to his couch instead, where he lay motionless, even as his possessions were packed up for transport around him.

At last, when his family had moved off into the distance and all was silent, the young brave began praying earnestly to his manitto, calling for his assistance in a plot to avenge himself on the maiden who had shunned and disgraced him. Before long, his prayer was answered, for his despondency began to ease and he felt impelled to move from lodge to lodge gathering up old scraps of cloth and personal ornaments left behind by his tribe. He took whatever he could find of these items outdoors and began sewing them into a coat and leggings which he trimmed elaborately with beads and feathers. Then he cast around him for any left-over animal bones and, after he had assembled these in the form of a human skeleton, began coating them with snow, pressing and smoothing it with his fingers until he had moulded the shape of a tall and handsome man. Again, he called upon his manitto for aid and, breathing upon the image, brought it to life. Next, he placed a bow and arrows in its hands and stood back to admire his creation of snow and rags.

'I will call you Moowis,' said the young man, delighted by the figure. 'Come handsome stranger, follow me, and I will explain to you why you have been sent here and how you are destined to help me.'

The two walked forward together in the direction of the tribe's summer camp. Their arrival generated tremendous excitement, not only because people were pleased to see the young brave returned to health, but also because they all desired to know the identity of his elegant companion. The chief of the tribe immediately invited the stranger to feast with his family that evening, while all the maidens of the camp lined up to catch even the slightest glimpse of him.

None was so infatuated by the striking visitor as the beautiful young maiden who had so haughtily refused the noble brave. Confidently, she strode forward and requested the company of her discarded lover and his companion at her lodge early that same afternoon. The two appeared at the appointed time and it seemed as if a transformation had occurred in the maiden, for she could not do enough to please the handsome stranger, even urging him to take up her father's place in the most comfortable chair by the fire. Not wishing to run the risk of melting during the visit, Moowis refused her kind offer, but this in itself was interpreted as the most humble and magnanimous of gestures. The noble brave smiled to see these things, for he knew that his plan was unfolding nicely and

Opposite:
'I will call you Moowis,' said the young man. 'Come, I will explain to you why you have been sent here and how you may help me.'

that, before long, the tribe would be celebrating a wedding feast.

On the following day, Moowis announced his intention to marry the beautiful young maiden and within a week the chief had proclaimed the couple man and wife. They remained very happy together for a short time, but then, one morning, Moowis turned to his wife and, gathering up his bow and arrows, declared that he must depart on a long and arduous journey.

'May I not come with you?' his wife pleaded.

But Moowis had been instructed by the young brave not to allow her to accompany him as punishment for her cruel actions towards him.

'The way is too difficult and dangerous,' Moowis told his bride. 'It is far better for you that you remain behind.'

'But there are no dangers I would not fully share with you,' she responded, stirring a wave of pity within her husband's breast. Disturbed and confused, Moowis went to his master's lodge and related to him his wife's request.

'It is good to see that she is so devoted to you,' the noble brave answered him, 'but she has never listened to the voice of prudence and still she will not listen. It is her own folly that drives her to accompany you and now she must submit to her fate.'

A rough and rugged road lay ahead for the newly wedded pair. The beautiful young wife was unaccustomed to hardship of any kind and it was not long before she had fallen behind, her feet torn and bleeding from the severe uphill struggle. Moowis continued his rapid pace, passing through thick, shady trees until he reached the broad, open plains. He had been long out of sight when the first rays of sun began to disperse the dull, grey clouds overhead, gradually warming the air and causing the snow to melt under his feet. Soon he observed a number of tiny glass beads appear on his white body, gently rolling to the ground through his fingers which had begun wasting away to reveal ivory-coloured bones. Moowis was helpless to prevent himself melting in the heat and, as he slowly dissolved, his splendid garments began to disintegrate also, dropping piece by piece on to the green grass below.

At length, the young bride arose and resumed her gruelling pursuit, crossing over rocks and marshland, until eventually she encountered fragments of clothing scattered on the earth. Quickly recognizing the tattered garments to be those of her husband, she was thrown into a frenzy of concern, but then, believing that some trick had been played on her, she began crying out:

'Moowis! Moowis! Nin ge won e win ig; ne won e wig!' (You have led me astray; I cannot find my way.) But the young wife received no reply. Now frantic with fear, she began running about wildly, through the forests, among the thickets, over the rocks, in every possible direction, hoping to catch sight of her handsome husband walking in the distance.

The years passed and still she roamed the countryside, calling aloud to the air, her face lined with exhaustion, her body stooped and twisted in sorrow. On and on she wandered until the day finally arrived for her to be released from her punishment. Falling wearily to the ground, she uttered her husband's name one last time before passing away. In an instant, her spirit rose from her body, ascending high above the spot in the deep recesses of the wood where she had eventually come to rest. But even to this day, it is said that her unhappy voice is often heard on the breeze, calling through the trees in search of her snow-husband:

'Moowis! Moowis! Nin ge won e win ig; ne won e wig!'

The Beaver Medicine Legend

NOPATSIS, SON OF A NOBLE INDIAN CHIEF, dwelt with his younger brother, Akaiyan, in a lodge at the foot of the mountains. Nopatsis was a well-meaning and gentle soul, but he did not share his brother's intelligence, and was renowned for the most impulsive behaviour.

One day he returned home accompanied by a young woman he proceeded to introduce to his younger brother as his wife. He knew little about her, he told Akaiyan, and was certain only of one thing, that he had fallen in love with her as soon as he had set eyes on her. Akaiyan welcomed the woman into their lodge, respecting his brother's choice, and did all that he could to make his new sister-in-law as comfortable as possible.

The weeks passed by quite smoothly, and the two brothers remained as close as they had always been since the day, many years before, when they had been tragically orphaned and left alone to care for each other. Nopatsis, although now a married man, always set aside time in the evenings to sit with his brother while the two discussed the day's events and watched the sun sinking into the clouds. The new wife was not so pleased to see this, however, and it was not long before she began pestering her husband to be rid of Akaiyan.

'He is my only brother,' Nopatsis explained to her, 'and I would not be parted from him for all the wealth in the world.'

But the young woman would not be put off by these words and decided that she must find a more devious way of persuading her husband to do as she wanted.

Her evil mind soon hit upon the perfect solution, and one day shortly afterwards, when she knew she had been left alone in the lodge with Akaiyan, she removed herself to her bedroom and began tearing at her clothes and clawing at her skin and hair. Nopatsis returned at sundown to find his wife sobbing and trembling by the door. In a quivering voice, she divulged to him that Akaiyan had treated her brutally, after having first sworn her to a silence she simply could not keep.

Nopatsis, whose misguided perception led him to accept all things at face value, was deeply disturbed by what he heard. Silently he listened, storing up hatred in his heart for his younger brother. Not once did he pause to consider that Akaiyan might be innocent; not once did he allow him an opportunity to defend himself. As his wife had planned it, Nopatsis became consumed by thoughts of revenge, debating in his mind night and day precisely how he would get rid of his brother.

The warmth of summer soon filled the air and with its arrival a large number of wild water-fowl gathered on the island of the great lake where it was customary for them to shed their brightly coloured feathers. Every year, the tribal warriors collected these feathers, using them to decorate their arrows. Nopatsis and Akaiyan now began making the raft that would take them to the island, binding logs together securely with strips of buffalo-hide. When their craft was ready, they set sail, reaching their destination before midday.

The two brothers agreed to separate in their search for feathers and Akaiyan wandered far off along the strand, stooping regularly to salvage the plumes washed up among the pebbles. Raising himself up from his crouched position after an interval of about ten minutes, he was astonished to see Nopatsis aboard their raft sailing back towards the mainland. He called out loudly to him:

Opposite: Nopatsis, although now a married man, always set aside time in the evenings to sit with his brother while the two watched the sun sinking in the clouds.

'Nopatsis, have you gone mad? What are you doing? Please return at once, I have no way of getting back home.'

But Nopatsis rowed onwards, hurling abuse at his brother for what he had done. Akaiyan protested and swore solemnly that he had not injured his sister-in-law in any way, but his cries were ignored all

the more and Nopatsis increased his speed, satisfied that he had served up a proper punishment.

Akaiyan sat down and wept bitterly, knowing that he would certainly perish on the island without food and clean drinking water. As night closed in, he began praying earnestly to the spirits of nature and to the sun and the moon for guidance, after which he felt a little more at ease. He took some branches and built himself a shelter, lining the earth with feathers on which he lay until sleep finally conquered his troubled spirit.

The next morning when he awoke he became aware of a little beaver standing in the doorway of his hut.

'My father would like you to visit him at his dwelling,' said the animal. 'I will lead you there if you care to follow.'

Akaiyan agreed to accept the invitation and promptly arose from his bed. Soon he approached a well-constructed lodge where Great Beaver, attended by his wife and family, waited to receive him. His host was indeed the most ancient and revered of all beavers, a wise old animal with a coat as white as snow and large, curling whiskers trailing the ground. Akaiyan immediately felt that he would be understood in such a place and he began to relate to Great Beaver the story of his ill-treatment.

The wise old animal listened and offered his sympathy and it was soon decided among the community that Akaiyan should spend the winter with them where he would be well cared for and introduced to a great many wonderful things he had never before experienced. Akaiyan was deeply touched by the family's kindness and when the beavers closed up their lodge for the winter he happily took up shelter with them. They kept him warm by placing their thick, fur-coated bodies alongside his and they taught him many secrets, including the art of healing, the planting and smoking of tobacco, and various sacred dances, songs and ceremonial prayers associated with the great mystery of medicine.

Summer returned and Akaiyan appeared above ground once more, hoping to find some way to reach the mainland. As luck would have it, his brother, Nopatsis, had set sail for the island that same morning intent on discovering whether or not his younger brother had survived the winter months. Akaiyan soon recognized the vessel, which now lay unattended, and quickly decided that fate might never again offer him a more favourable opportunity. Racing towards Great Beaver's lodge, he entered one last time and sadly took leave of his friends.

'Choose something to take with you as a parting gift,' Great Beaver urged him, 'some small item you may remember us by.' Gazing around him, Akaiyan's eyes fell upon Great Beaver's youngest child with whom he had formed a very special bond during his stay. At first, the wise old animal would not agree to Akaiyan's request, for he prized his little one above all other things, but finally he surrendered to the wishes of both Akaiyan and his pleading child, counselling Little Beaver to construct a sacred Beaver Bundle as soon as he arrived on the mainland.

Akaiyan was soon walking towards his native village in the company of Little Beaver. Many of the warriors he had hunted with in the past ran forward to greet him, surprised and relieved to see him alive. They longed to hear of his adventures and soon the chief had ordered a great fire to be lit, around which they all sat as Akaiyan told them his story. Little Beaver then stood up and proceeded to explain to the people, as his father had bid him, the mystery of medicine with its accompanying songs and sacred dances. He called for a Beaver Bundle to be made and to this each man contributed a relic conveying good or ill luck, including feathers, animal-skins, bones, rocks and stone-pipes. Long into the evening, they watched Little Beaver as he danced, and many chiefs of the animal tribes joined in the ceremony, honoured to receive the Beaver Medicine that had been brought to them from the island.

When he was satisfied that he had accomplished his task of instruction, Little Beaver agreed to be returned to his parents. On the island, Akaiyan found the bones of his vengeful brother and was grateful that he had escaped a fate intended for him. Great Beaver presented the young warrior with a sacred pipe in exchange for his child and taught him the songs and dances that would speed the growth of the tobacco plants on the plains.

Every spring Akaiyan set off on his little raft to visit the beavers, and on each occasion he received some important object to add to his Beaver Medicine Bundle, until it reached a great size, bringing him prosperity and good fortune. Soon afterwards, he married a wholesome woman and together they founded a race of medicine-men who never failed to pass on the traditions and ceremonials of the Beaver Medicine to their own offspring, ensuring that the good works of Akaiyan and Little Beaver have remained with us even to this day.

The Legend of Scar-face[1]

IN A FAR-OFF TIME, there lived an Indian who had a very beautiful daughter. Many young warriors desired to marry her, but at each request, she only shook her head and said she had no need of a husband.

'Why is this?' asked her father. A great many of these young men are rich and handsome, yet still you refuse them.'

'Why should I marry?' replied the girl, 'when I have all that I could possibly want here with you at our lodge.'

'It is a shame for us,' said her mother, 'that we should still have an unmarried daughter. People will begin to believe you keep a secret lover.'

At this, the girl bowed her head and addressed her parents solemnly: 'I have no secret lover, I promise you, but now hear the truth. The Sun-god above has decreed that I cannot marry and he has told me that I will live happily, to a great age, if I preserve myself for him alone.'

'Ah!' replied her father, 'if the Sun-god has spoken thus, then his wishes must be obeyed. It is not for us to question the ways of the gods.'

In a nearby village there dwelt a poor young warrior who had neither parents nor relatives. Left to fend for himself, he had become a mighty hunter with a brave and noble spirit. He would have been a very good-looking young man, but for a long scar on his cheek, left by the claw of a great grizzly bear he had slain in close combat. The other warriors of the village had ostracized the youth because of this disfigurement. They had given him the name of Scar-face and nothing pleased them more than to make a mockery of his appearance. Each of these young men had been unsuccessful in their attempt to win the hand of the beautiful young maiden and now, slightly embittered by failure, they made it an occasion to poke some fun at the poor, deformed youth.

'Why don't you ask that girl to marry you,' they taunted him. 'She could hardly refuse a man like you, so rich and handsome.'

They laughed a great deal to see that they had touched upon a sensitive nerve, for Scar-face blushed from ear to ear at their suggestion and stared longingly in the direction of the young woman's lodge.

Opposite:
Each of the young men had been unsuccessful in their attempt to woo the maiden. Now they made it an occasion to poke some fun at the deformed youth.

'I will go and do as you say,' he suddenly replied and marched off defiantly towards the river to deliver his proposal.

He found the young woman stooping by the banks gathering rushes. Respectfully, he approached her, and as she gazed upon him with bright, enticing eyes, he shyly announced his purpose: 'I know

that I am poor and shabbily dressed,' he told her, 'but I have seen you refuse rich men clothed in luxurious fur. I am not handsome either, but you have shunned men of the noblest features. Would you consider having me for your husband? I cannot promise you wealth, but I can promise you love, as much of it as you care to receive from me.'

The young girl lowered her eyes and stared silently into the shallow water. After a time she turned towards Scar-face and spoke softly: 'It little matters to me that you are poor. My father is wealthy and would happily provide for us both. I am glad that a man of courage has finally asked me to marry him. But wait! I cannot accept your offer, for the Sun-god has reserved me for himself and has declared that I may never take a mortal husband. Seek him out, if you truly care for me, and beg him to release me from this covenant. If he agrees to do this, ask him to remove that scar from your face and I will treat it as a sign of his blessing.'

Scar-face was sad at heart to hear these words. He had no idea where to begin his search for the Sun-god and felt that a deity so powerful would almost certainly refuse to surrender to him his intended bride. But the young warrior had never before recoiled from a challenge, no matter how difficult it appeared, and the prospect of such a glorious reward seemed well worth risking his life for.

For many days and many nights he journeyed over the sweeping prairies and on through the dense forests, carrying a small sack of food, a spare pair of moccasins, and a simple bow and arrow. Every day his sack of food grew lighter, but he saved as much as he could, eating wild berries and roots and sometimes killing a small bird. At length, he came across a bear's cave and paused to ask directions to the lodge of the Sun-god.

'I have travelled far and wide,' the bear told him, 'but I have never come across the Sun-god's lodge. Stripe-face, who lives beyond in that hole, may be able to assist you. Go and ask him for his help.'

Scar-face moved towards the hole and stooping over it, called aloud to the animal within: 'O generous Stripe-face, O wise old badger, can you tell me the way to the lodge of the Sun-god?'

'I am old and frail and never journey very far,' replied the badger. 'I do not know where he lives. Over there, through the trees, you will find a wolverine. Go and speak with him.'

Scar-face obeyed the badger's instructions, but having called aloud for several minutes, he could find no trace of the wolverine. Wearily, he sat on the ground and began to examine what remained of his food: 'Pity me, wolverine,' he cried out despondently, 'my moccasins are worn through, my food is almost gone. Take pity on me, or I shall meet my death here.'

'How can I help you,' said a voice, and turning around, Scar-face came face to face with the wolverine.

'I have travelled a great distance in search of the Sun-god,' he told the animal, 'but no one can tell me where he lives.'

'I can show you where he lives,' replied the wolverine, 'but first you must rest, for the journey is long. Tomorrow, as soon as you awake, I will set you on the right path.'

Early the next morning, the wolverine took Scar-face to the edge of the forest and pointed out the trail he should follow. Scar-face set off and walked many miles until he came upon the shores of a vast lake whose waters stretched as far as the eye could see. His spirits fell at this sight, for the great lake presented him with a problem he could not hope to overcome.

'I cannot cross this black and fearful water,' he said to himself, 'and I do not have the strength to return home to my own people. The end has come and I must give up the fight.'

But help was not so very far away and soon two beautiful white swans advanced towards him on the water.

'You are not far from the object of your search,' they called to him. 'Lie on our backs and we will carry you to the other side.'

Scar-face rose up and waded into the water. Before long, he had safely reached dry land where he thanked the swans and began following once more the broad trail leading to the home of the Sun-god.

It was now past midday and still the young warrior had not reached his destination. But he refused to lose hope and before long his optimism was rewarded, for he soon stumbled upon an array of beautiful objects lying in the earth which he knew must be from another world. He had never seen such splendid, golden-tipped arrows, or a war shield so elaborately decorated with beads and precious stones. He felt tempted to remove these items from the earth, but decided that would be dishonourable of him, and tried to picture instead what the owner of such fine weapons might look like. He had moved a little further onwards when he observed quite the handsomest youth he had ever seen approaching in the distance. The young man wore clothing of the smoothest animal skin and moccasins sewn with brightly coloured feathers.

'I am searching for my bow and arrows, have you seen them?' the beautiful stranger inquired.

'Yes, I have seen them, back there, lying on the ground,' replied Scar-face.

'And you did not wish to seize these items for yourself?' the young man asked.

'No,' answered Scar-face, 'I felt that would be wrong of me. I knew that the owner would eventually return for them.'

'I admire your honesty, and you have saved me a tiring search,' said the stranger. 'Where is it you come from? You appear to be a very long way from home.'

'I am looking for the Sun-god,' Scar-face told him, 'and I believe I am not very far from his house.'

'You are right,' replied the handsome youth. 'The Sun-god is my father and I am Apisirahts, the Morning Star. Come, I will take you to my father's lodge. He will be pleased to meet a man of such honest character.'

They set off together and shortly afterwards Morning Star pointed to a great lodge, basked in glorious golden light, whose walls were covered with magnificent paintings of medicine animals and other rare and curious creatures. At the entrance to the lodge stood a beautiful woman, Morning Star's mother, Kikomikis, the Moon-goddess. She embraced her son and welcomed the footsore traveller into their home. Then, the great Sun-god made his appearance and he too greeted Scar-face kindly, inviting him to stay for as long as he needed and urging him to accept the guidance and friendship of his son, Apisirahts.

'He will show you the wonderful sights of our kingdom,' the Sun-god told Scar-face. 'Go with him wherever you please, but never hunt near the Great Water, for that is the home of the savage birds who bear talons as long as spears and bills as sharp as arrows. They have carried off many of our finest warriors and would not hesitate to kill you both.'

Scar-face listened carefully to all that was said and during the months which followed, he lived happily among his celestial friends, learning to love the Sun-god as a father and becoming more and more intimate with Apisirahts whom he came to regard as the brother he had always longed for in his earthly home.

One day, he set off with Apisirahts on a hunting excursion, but the two did not follow their usual route and soon they found themselves by the shores of the Great Water.

'We are the finest hunters in the kingdom,' said Morning Star, 'so let us wait no longer, but go and kill these savage birds that put terror into the hearts of our people.'

Opposite:
'He will show you the wonderful sights of our kingdom,' the Sun-god told Scar-face. 'Go with him wherever you please, but never hunt near the Great Water.'

'Your father has already told us not to pursue them,' replied Scar-face, 'and I have promised to heed his warning.'

'Then I will go and hunt them alone,' said Morning Star and he jumped into the water, waving his spear and shouting his war-cry. Scar-face was forced to follow, for he did not wish to see his brother come to any harm. Soon he had overtaken Apisirahts and began lashing out boldly with his weapon, slaying the monstrous creatures that swooped down upon him, attempting to sink their barbed claws into his flesh. When he had slaughtered every last one of them, he severed their heads and the two young men carried these back towards the Sun-god's lodge, anxious to relate the details of their heroic conquest.

The Moon-goddess was shocked to see the carcasses of the savage birds and scolded her son for his foolishness. But at the same time, she was relieved that Morning Star had escaped unharmed and ran to inform the Sun-god of his safe return, instinctively aware that she had Scar-face to thank for her son's safe delivery.

'I will not forget what you have done for us this day,' the Sun-god told Scar-face. 'If I can ever repay you, you must let me know at once and whatever you request of me shall be brought to you.'

Scar-face hesitated only a moment and then began to explain to the god the reason for his long journey away from home.

'You have never greedily demanded anything of us,' said the god, 'and you have suffered patiently all these months a great burden of anxiety, knowing that I alone have the power to decide your future with a woman you love and admire so earnestly. Your kindness and your patience have earned the young maiden her freedom. Return home now and make her your wife.

'One thing I will ask of you, however, when you return to your home. Build a lodge in honour of me, shape it like the world, round with thick walls, and paint it red so that every day you will be reminded of your visit here. It shall be a great Medicine Lodge and if your wife remains pure and true I will always be there to help you in times of illness or hardship.'

Then the god explained to Scar-face many of the intricacies of Sun-medicine and rubbed a powerful remedy into the skin on his cheek which caused his unsightly scar to disappear instantly. The young warrior was now ready to return home and the Moon-goddess gave him many beautiful gifts to take to his people. The Sun-god pointed to a short route through the Milky Way and soon he had reached the earth, ready to enter his village in triumph.

It was a very hot day and the sun shone brilliantly in the sky, forcing the people to shed their clothing and sit in the shade. Towards midday, when the heat was at its fiercest, the chief of the village peered through the window of his lodge and caught sight of a figure, wrapped from head to foot in thick animal skins, sitting on a butte nearby.

'Who is that strange person sitting in winter clothing? The heat will certainly kill him, for I see that he has no food or water. Go and invite him to sit indoors with us.'

Some of the villagers approached the stranger and called to him: 'Our chief is concerned for you. He wishes you to withdraw to the shade of his lodge.'

But they had no sooner spoken these words when the figure arose and flung his outer garments to the ground. The robe he wore underneath was of the most delicate, embroidered cloth and the weapons he carried were of an extraordinary, gleaming metal. Gazing upon the stranger's face, the villagers recognized in it something familiar, and at last, one of them cried out in surprise: 'It is Scar-face, the poor young warrior we thought had been lost forever. But look, the blemish on his face has disappeared.'

All the people rushed forward to examine the young man for themselves.

'Where have you been?' they asked excitedly. 'Who gave you all these beautiful things?'

But the handsome warrior did not answer. His eyes searched instead through the crowd until they fell upon the beautiful face of the maiden he had returned home to marry.

'The trail was long and tortuous,' he told her as he walked boldly forward, 'but I found the lodge of the Sun-god and I won his favour. He has taken away my scar and given me all these things as proof of his consent. Come with me now and be my wife for that is the Sun-god's greatest wish.'

The maiden ran towards him and fell upon his breast, tears of great joy flowing freely down her cheeks. That same day the young couple were married and before long they had raised a great Medicine Lodge to the Sun-god. During the long years ahead, they were never sick or troubled in any way and were blessed with two fine, strong children, a girl and a boy, whom they named Apisirahts and Kikomikis.

1 This legend is attributed to the famous Blackfeet tribe of the western territories.

✳   ✳   ✳

THE SUN ENSNARED
AND OTHER LEGENDS

HOSEN FROM AMONG the ancient folklore of a number of widely scattered tribes, the stories which follow are a very broad selection of some of the most popular and characteristic of native American legends. These are tales which, centuries ago, occupied a prime position in the tribal story-teller's repertoire, tales that would have been recited to the young and old around the lodge-fires and handed down in an oral form from generation to generation, becoming more exaggerated and colourful with each retelling.

The mythology which evolved in this way is a richly varied one, preserving a striking image of a traditional native American culture before the arrival of European settlers in their homeland. Native American man believed emphatically in the existence of supernatural forces, both good and evil, and sought communion with nature as the most fruitful path to self-fulfilment. Animals had the power to turn into people and people into animals; each individual was protected by a patron guardian spirit; and every object of creation, animate and inanimate, possessed life and consciousness.

The nine tales retold here illustrate well many of the popular superstitions of this patient and industrious people who lived happily as caretakers of the earth, promoting the unity and continuity of all life.

The Sun Ensnared

AT THE VERY BEGINNING OF TIME, when chaos and darkness reigned and hordes of bloodthirsty animals roamed the earth devouring mankind, there remained only two survivors of the human race. A young brother and sister, who managed to flee from the jaws of the ferocious beasts, took refuge in a secluded part of the forest where they built for themselves a little wooden lodge. Here, they carved out a meagre existence, relying on nature's kindness for their survival. The young girl, who was strong and hardworking, bravely accepted the responsibility of keeping the household together, for her younger brother had never grown beyond the size of an infant and demanded her constant care. Every morning she would go out in search of firewood, taking her brother with her and seating him on a comfortable bed of leaves while she chopped and stacked the logs they needed to keep a warm fire burning. Then, before heading homeward, she would gather the ripest berries from the surrounding hedgerows and both would sit down together to enjoy their first meal of the day.

They had passed many pleasant years in this way before the young girl began to grow anxious for her brother's future, fearing that she might not always be able to care for him. She had never considered it wise in the past to leave him alone while she went about her chores, but now she felt she must take that risk for his own good.

'Little brother,' she said to him, 'I will leave you behind today while I go out to gather wood, but you need not be afraid and I promise to return shortly.'

And saying this, she handed him a bow and several small arrows.

'Hide yourself behind that bush,' she added, 'and soon you will see a snowbird coming to pick worms from the newly cut logs. When the bird appears, try your skill and see if you can shoot it.'

Delighted at the opportunity to prove himself, the young boy sat down excitedly, ready to draw his bow as soon as the bird alighted on the logs. But the first arrow he shot went astray and before he was able to launch a second, the creature had risen again into the air. The little brother felt *Opposite: But his* | defeated and discouraged and bowed his head in shame, fully expecting *sister's words only* | that his sister would mock his failure. As soon as she returned, however, *added to the boy's* | she began to reassure him, offering him encouragement and insisting *curiosity, and he grew* | that he try again on the following day. *more impatient than* *ever to slip away and* | Next morning, the little brother crouched down once more *explore the land for* *himself.*

behind the bush and waited for the snowbird to appear. He was now more determined than ever to prove his skill and, on this occasion, his arrow shot swiftly through the air, piercing the bird's breast. Seeing his sister approach in the distance, he ran forward to meet her, his face beaming with pride and joy.

'I have killed a fine, large bird,' he announced triumphantly. 'Please will you skin it for me and stretch the skin out to dry in the sunshine. When I have killed more birds, there will be enough skins to make me a fine, long coat.'

'I would be very happy to do this for you,' his sister smiled. 'But what shall I do with the body when I have skinned it?'

The young boy searched for an answer, and as he stood thinking his stomach groaned with hunger. It seemed wasteful to burn such a plump bird and he now began to wonder what it would be like to taste something other than wild berries and greens: 'We have never before eaten flesh,' he said, 'but let us cut the body in two and cook one half of it in a pot over the fire. Then, if the food is good, we can savour the remaining half later.'

His sister agreed that this was a wise decision and prepared for them their very first dish of game which they both ate with great relish that same evening.

The little brother had passed his very first test of manhood and with each passing day he grew more confident of his ability to survive in the wilderness. Soon he had killed ten birds whose skins were sewn into the coat he had been promised. Fiercely proud of his hunting skills, he wore this new garment both day and night and felt himself ready to meet any challenge life might throw at him.

'Are we really all alone in the world, sister?' he asked one day as he paraded up and down the lodge in his bird-skin coat, 'since I cannot believe that this great broad earth with its fine blue sky was created simply for the pair of us.'

'There may be other people living,' answered his sister, 'but they can only be terrible beings, very unlike us. It would be most unwise to go in search of these people, little brother, and you must never be tempted to stray too far from home.'

But his sister's words only added to the young boy's curiosity, and he grew more impatient than ever to slip away quietly and explore the surrounding forests and countryside for himself.

Before the sun had risen on the following morning, he grabbed his bow and arrows and set off enthusiastically in the direction of the open hills. By midday, he had walked a very great distance, but still he hadn't discovered any other human beings. At length, he decided to rest for a while and lay down on the grass in the warmth of the sun's golden rays. He had happened upon a very beautiful spot, and was soon lulled gently to sleep by the tinkling sound of the waters dancing over the pebbles of a nearby stream. He slept for many hours in the heat of the brilliant sunshine and would have remained in this position a good while longer had he not been disturbed by the sensation that something close to him had begun to shrink and shrivel. At first, he thought he had been dreaming, but as he opened his eyes wider and gazed upon his bird-skin coat, he soon realized that it had tightened itself upon his body, so much so that he was scarcely able to breathe.

The young boy stood up in horror and began to examine his seared and singed coat more closely. The garment he had been so proud of was now totally ruined and he flew into a great passion, vowing to take vengeance on the sun for what it had done.

'Do not imagine that you can escape me because you are so high up in the sky,' he shouted angrily. 'What you have done will not go unpunished. I will pay you back before long.' And after he had sworn this oath, he trudged back home wearily to tell his sister of the dreadful misfortune that had befallen his new coat.

The young girl was now more worried than ever for her little brother. Ever since his return, he had fallen into a deep depression, refusing all food and laying down on his side, as still as a corpse, for a full ten days, at the end of which he turned over and lay on his other side for a further ten days. When he eventually arose, he was pale and drawn, but his voice was firm and resolute as he informed his sister that she must make a snare for him with which he intended to catch the sun.

'Find me some material suitable for making a noose,' he told her, but when his sister returned with a piece of dried deer sinew, he shook his head and said it would not do. Racking her brains, she searched again through their belongings, and came forward with a bird skin, left over from the coat she had made.

'This won't do either, 'her brother declared agitatedly, 'the sun has had enough of my bird skins already. Go and find me something else.'

Finally, his sister thought of her own beautiful long hair, and pulling several glossy strands from her head, she began to weave a thick black cord which she handed to her brother.

'This is exactly what I need,' he said delightedly and began to draw it back and forth through his fingers until it grew rigid and strong. Then, having coiled it round his shoulders, he kissed his sister goodbye and set off to catch the sun, just as the last light began to fade in the sky.

Under cover of darkness, the little brother set his trap, fixing the snare on a spot where he knew the sun would first strike the land as it rose above the earth. He waited patiently, offering up many prayers. These were answered as soon as the sun attempted to rise from its sleepy bed, for it became fastened to the ground by the cord and could not ascend any higher. No light twinkled on the horizon and the land remained in deep shadow, deprived of the sun's warm rays.

Fear and panic erupted among the animals who ruled the earth as they awoke to discover a world totally submerged in darkness. They ran about blindly, calling to each other, desperate to find some explanation for what had happened. The most powerful among them immediately formed a council and it was agreed that someone would have to go forward to the edge of the horizon to investigate why the sun had not risen. This was a very dangerous undertaking, since whoever ventured so close to the sun risked severe burning and possible death. Only the dormouse, at that time the largest animal in the world, taller than any mountain, stood up bravely, offering to risk her life so that the others might be saved.

Hurriedly, she made her way to the place where the sun lay captive and quickly spotted the cord pinning it to the ground. Even now, though the dormouse was not yet close enough to begin gnawing the cord, her back began to smoke and the intense heat was almost overwhelming. Still she persevered, chewing the cord with her two front teeth while at the same time her huge bulk was turned into an enormous heap of ashes. When, at last, the sun was freed, it shot up into the sky as dazzling as it had ever been. But the dormouse, now shrunken to become one of the tiniest creatures in the world, fled in terror from its light and from that day forward she became known as Kug-e-been-gwa-kwa, or Blind Woman.

As soon as he discovered that the sun had escaped his snare, the little brother returned home once more to his sister. But he was now no longer anxious to take revenge, since his adventure had brought him greater wisdom and the knowledge that he had not been born to

Opposite:
A council was formed and it was agreed that one of their number would have to go to the edge of the horizon to investigate why the sun had not risen.

interfere with the ways of nature. For the rest of his life, he devoted himself to hunting, and within a very short time had shot enough snowbirds to make himself a new coat, even finer than the one which had led him to challenge the sun.

The Serpent-men

AFTER OVER A MONTH ON THE WAR-PATH, an eminent band of Sioux warriors accompanied by their chief, were returning home to their encampment in the hills. When they were still quite a long way off, they were suddenly gripped by a savage hunger and decided amongst themselves to scatter in search of wild game to sustain them on the rest of their journey. Some dispersed to the woodlands while others headed for the plains, agreeing that the first to locate an animal should signal to the others to join in the pursuit, for no great warrior could ever enjoy the flesh of a creature he had not helped to track down.

They had been on the hunt for some time without having anything to show for their efforts when suddenly one of the braves, placing his ear to the ground, declared that he could hear a herd of buffalo approaching in the distance. The prospect of such an enjoyable chase greatly cheered the young warriors and they gathered around their chief, anxious to assist in the plan to intercept the animals.

Closer and closer came the sound of the herd. The chief and his men lay very still in the undergrowth, their arrows poised and ready to shoot as soon as the buffalo came into view. Suddenly, their target appeared, but to their absolute horror the group came face to face, not with the four-legged animals they had been expecting, but with a gigantic snake, its rattle held menacingly in the air, as large as a man's head. Although almost paralysed with terror, the chief somehow managed to raise his weapon and shot an arrow through the air which lodged itself in the snake's throat. The huge creature immediately keeled over and lay squirming and hissing in the earth for some minutes until all life had passed out of it.

Even though it lay dead, the Sioux warriors did not dare to approach the snake for quite some time but remained instead at a safe distance, debating what they should do with the carcass. Hunger beckoned once more and for the first time the chief was struck by the thought that they had, in fact, provided themselves with a perfectly good, if unusual, meal. He called up his men and ordered them to build a fire and soon they were helping themselves to a delicious stew, as flavoursome as the tenderest buffalo meat. Only one brave refused to partake of the meal. Even his extreme hunger could not conquer his scruples and he remained adamant that he would not join the others in tasting the body of a great rattling snake.

Opposite:
A savage hunger descended on the band of Sioux warriors. They agreed to go in search of wild game to sustain them on the rest of their journey.

When the meal was over, the warriors felt both satisfied and drowsy and lay down beside the camp-fire for a brief rest in preparation for their ongoing journey. It was several hours before the chief awoke, but as he slowly opened his eyes, he imagined he must still be dreaming, for he observed that all around him, his men had turned to snakes. Then he gazed at his own body and cried out in alarm, for he himself was already half snake, half man. Hastily, he slithered towards his transformed warriors and observed that only one among them had not suffered the same fate as the others – the young brave who had earlier refused to try any of the food.

The serpent-men and their chief placed themselves under the protection of the young brave, requesting that he gather them together in a large robe and carry them to the summit of the high hill overlooking their village. Terrified by the sight of them and fearing he might soon be attacked, the boy raced all the way to the hill-top and flung the robe beneath some trees. But the snakes broke free quickly and, moving towards him, coiled themselves around his ankles. They had no wish to harm him, they assured him, and soon he discovered that they treated him very kindly, sharing with him their strange wisdom and their many mysterious charms.

'You must return to the village and visit our families for us,' they said to him. 'Tell the people not to be afraid, and say to our wives and children that we shall visit them in the summer when they should come out to greet us.'

The young brave readily agreed to deliver this message and set off homewards without further delay. Tears filled the eyes of every villager as he informed them of the fate of their chief and the other great warriors of the tribe, but the people were determined not to let grief destroy them, and took some comfort in the news that they would at least see their loved ones again.

It was a hot summer's morning when the snakes arrived at the little village, striking up a loud, hissing chorus that immediately attracted the attention of every man, woman and child. Abruptly, the villagers gathered together and walked cautiously in the direction of the snakes, taking with them moccasins, leggings, saddles and weapons that once belonged to the missing warriors. Their hearts were filled with fear as they drew closer to the creatures and they stood, still at a safe distance, fully prepared to turn on their heels. But the chief, who sat at the centre of the serpent-men, rose up from the earth and spoke to his people reassuringly: 'Do not be afraid of us,' he called to them. 'Do not flee from us, we mean you no harm.'

From that moment, the people grew in confidence and moving boldly forwards, they formed a circle around the serpent-men and chatted to them long into the evening.

In the winter the snakes vanished altogether, but every summer, for as long as the villagers could remember, they returned, wearing a new and brilliant coat. The villagers always treated them with the greatest respect and taught their children to revere the serpent, so that even today if a snake appears in the pathway of a tribal warrior, he will always stop and talk to it, offering it some token of his friendship and regard.

The Sacred Bundle

IN A CERTAIN VILLAGE OF THE PAWNEE TRIBE, there lived a vain young man who always insisted upon wearing the finest clothes and the richest ornaments, no matter how ordinary and uneventful the day that lay ahead. Although unmarried and extremely handsome, he showed no interest in the maidens of the village, but concentrated exclusively on improving his hunting skills, inviting himself to join whatever party happened to be planning an excursion. Among his most prized possessions, he had the down feather of an eagle which he always wore on his head, believing it possessed strange magical properties.

One morning, while he was out hunting, the young man became separated from his companions and, to pass the time, he began following a herd of buffalo for some considerable distance. The animals eventually scattered, with the exception of a young cow, who had become stuck in a mud-hole. Pleased that fate had presented him with such a favourable target, the young man raised his bow and arrow and was about to take aim when he noticed the cow had disappeared, and in its place stood a beautiful young woman. The hunter remained deeply perplexed, for he could not understand where the animal had disappeared to, nor could he comprehend where the maiden had suddenly sprung from.

Warily, he approached the girl, but was surprised to find that she was most friendly towards him and that her presence filled him with a strange delight he had never before experienced. The two sat down and chatted together for many hours, and so enamoured was the hunter by the end of this time that he asked the young maiden to marry him and return with him to his tribe. Graciously she consented, but only on the condition that they set up home in the precise spot where he had discovered her.

To this, the hunter readily agreed and removed from around his neck a string of blue and white beads which he gave to his new wife as a wedding gift.

The two lived very happily together for many months until the evening the young man returned home after a day's hunting to find his lodge surrounded by the marks of many hooves and not a trace of his wife in sight. For weeks he scoured the woodlands and neighbouring countryside, but still he could not discover any sign of her whereabouts. Defeated and dejected, he resolved that he had no option but to return to his own tribe in an attempt to rebuild something of the life he had left behind.

The years passed by, and even though he had a great many offers of marriage, the handsome young man refused to choose for himself a new bride. Try as he might, he could not remove from his mind an image of the beautiful maiden and he mourned her loss with an ever-increasing passion.

One summer's morning, however, as he stood chatting to a number of his friends, he noticed a young boy walking towards him. The child wore around his neck a string of blue and white beads and his clothing revealed that he had come from a distant village.

'Father,' said the boy, 'mother would like to speak to you.'

Annoyed by the interruption, the young hunter replied curtly: 'I am not your father, go away and do not pester me.'

The boy went away, and the hunter's companions began laughing loudly, amused by the fact that the man whose reputation for spurning women was famous throughout the village should ever have been addressed as 'father'. But at length the boy returned only to repeat exactly the same words. He was again dismissed in an angry fashion, but still he did not give up. On the third occasion when he reappeared, some of the men suggested that it might be a good idea for the hunter to follow the child to see what he wanted. This seemed a sensible suggestion and so he set off on the trail of the boy, keen to get to the bottom of the mystery once and for all.

The blue and white beads he had spotted around the boy's neck had begun to agitate the hunter. He could not place them exactly, but then, up ahead, he saw a buffalo cow with her calf running across the prairie and

Opposite: The young man began following a herd of buffalo. The animals eventually scattered, with the exception of a young cow, who had become stuck in the mud.

suddenly he began to remember the clearest details of his former life. Taking his bow and arrows, he followed the buffalo whom he now recognized as his wife and child. But the woman, angry that her husband had not come when he had been repeatedly summoned, made sure that the chase was long and wearisome. She dried up every

creek they came to, so that the hunter feared he would die of thirst, and frightened off any deer he attempted to pursue, so that he grew pale and weak with hunger. But for the kindness of his child, the young man might well have perished, but the boy took pity on him and managed to obtain food and drink at intervals, enough to sustain the hunter until they arrived at the home of the buffalo.

The leader of the herd, who was father of the buffalo cow, had never approved of his daughter's marriage and it was he who had kidnapped her from the nuptial home many years before. His resentment was still as strong as it had ever been, and as soon as he laid eyes on the young man, he desired only to kill him. But at last, after lengthy deliberations, the great chief agreed that the hunter would be free to live if he survived a number of rigorous trials designed by the elders of the herd.

To begin with, six cows were placed in a row before the hunter, and he was told that his life would be spared if he could identity his wife among them. It was an impossible feat, since each of the cows was almost identical in appearance to the next, but once again the young child intervened to help his father, and secretly indicated to him where his mother stood in the parade. The old bulls were more than surprised at his success, but very irritated at the same time, and insisted that the hunter surrender himself to a second test. This time, they lined up six buffalo calves and asked him to pick out his son from among them. But the hunter felt certain that his son would give him some small clue to his identity, and so, when one of the calves swished its tail high in the air, the hunter pointed to it and successfully located his own son.

The leader of the herd still remained dissatisfied and was determined to rid himself of the intruder even though he had passed all of their tests. Having promised the young man that he would now bring his wife to him, he asked him to sit on the ground until he had returned with his daughter. The hunter had no sooner complied with this request however, when he heard a noise like thunder approaching, and looking up, he saw the entire buffalo herd rushing towards him. One by one the buffalo charged past the spot, coming to a halt only after they felt satisfied that they had trampled him to pieces. But when they turned around to examine their mighty work, they were astonished to find the young hunter sitting calmly in the centre of the circle, a white feather proudly positioned in his hair.

The chief bull, who had never imagined his son-in-law to possess such magical powers, now moved forward respectfully and

Opposite: After lengthy deliberations, the great chief agreed that the hunter might live if he survived a number of rigorous trials designed by the elders.

lifted him off the ground. He had won back his buffalo-wife and child, the chief told him, but there remained one final thing for him to do before he could be welcomed into the buffalo camp. He must go off and gather together a selection of gifts from his tribe and bring them back to the buffalo herd as a mark of his respect.

The young man set off with his wife and son towards his village making a list in his mind of the fine things he intended to gather together to impress the buffalo chief – corn, maize, the finest fruit and the most succulent deer-flesh. But when he arrived at his home, he was shocked to discover that there was no food to be had, for a great famine had descended upon the people causing many to die of starvation. The buffalo-wife, who was quick to notice the distress her husband suffered, quietly withdrew from his company, and it was not long before she reappeared, pulling from under her robe a great slab of buffalo meat which she presented to the starving people. Every day for a whole month she repeated this act of kindness so that the people soon recovered their strength and began to smile anew. As a way of thanking the young man and his wife, they gathered together the very best of their possessions to present to the buffalo chief and sent the family on its way once more, back to the great camp.

But having returned home, the young son could not rest, knowing his father's people were constantly in want of food. At length, he went and spoke with his grandfather, the chief of the herd, and soon they had worked out a solution to the problem.

Transforming himself into a buffalo, the young boy led the whole herd back towards the village, accompanied by his mother and father in human shape. When they had reached their destination, the father, as his son had commanded him, addressed the people with the following words:

'From this day forward you may hunt the buffalo for food, but you must not kill my son, who is among them, for it is he who generously provides you with the yellow calf.

'The time will come when you will be directed to kill the yellow calf and sacrifice it to the god Tirawa. Then you must tan its hide and form a bundle of its skin, placing within it an ear of corn and other things sacred to your tribe.

'Every year, you must look among the herd for another yellow calf. This too, you should sacrifice and keep a piece of its flesh to add to the bundle. Then, whenever food is scarce and famine threatens, you must gather in council around your sacred bundle and

Opposite:
As a way of thanking the young man and his wife, the villagers presented them with the very best of their possessions .

pray to Tirawa who will answer your need, and send another yellow calf to you.'

All this was done as the young boy had instructed, and before long food became plentiful and the father rose to become a chief, greatly respected by the people. He lived for many long and happy years among the villagers with his buffalo-wife and when he died the sacred bundle was long preserved and guarded religiously by the tribe who always used it in times of need as a magic charm to bring the buffalo.

The Origin of the Three Races

HAVING RESOLVED TO CREATE A NEW SPECIES, the Great Spirit took himself off to a place of solitude and began the labour that was to last him several days. He toiled long and hard and at length he produced a being, different from anything else he had ever before created. The figure, whose skin was black as the night, enthralled the Great Spirit, and at first he was deeply satisfied with his work. But soon, he felt that a single example of the new species was not enough and he decided to embark upon a second attempt, hopeful that the result would bring him equal pleasure.

On the next occasion, his creation proved to be a being with a red skin colour. Placing him alongside his brother, the Great Spirit smiled. He was even more pleased with the fruits of his labour, but once again, after only a short time, he became anxious to try his hand a third time.

'This will be my last effort,' he told himself, and he wandered off to complete his final creation. The being he produced this time had a white skin colour, far lighter than the other two. It proved to be the Great Spirit's favourite, and so utterly satisfied him that he spent several minutes turning it over in the palm of his hand before releasing it to the company of its two elder brothers.

Calling the three men before him one day soon afterwards, the Great Spirit pointed to three boxes lying in the earth. The first box contained books, papers and quills; the second was filled with bows and arrows, tomahawks and spears; the third held a collection of spades, axes, hoes and hammers. The Great Spirit then addressed his children with these words:

'My sons, what you see before you are the means by which you shall live. Each of you must choose one of the boxes for your future use.' And saying this, he beckoned to his favourite, the white man, instructing him to make the first choice.

The youngest brother passed by the working-tools, the axes, hoes and hammers, without paying them any attention whatsoever and moved towards the weapons of war and hunting. Here, he hesitated, lifting a number of them from the box so that he might examine them more closely. The red-skinned brother trembled, for with his whole heart he longed to take possession of these instruments and feared that he was close to losing them. But the white man deliberated only a moment longer and then passed swiftly on to the box of books and writing tools, signalling to the Great Spirit that he had finally reached his decision.

The red-skinned brother came next, and he sprang forward and immediately seized upon the bows and arrows, the tomahawks and spears, delighted with himself that he was now the owner of so valuable a collection.

Last of all, the black man stepped forward, the Great Spirit's first offspring. Having no choice left, he lifted the remaining box filled with tools of the land and humbly carried it all the way back to his dwelling.

It was in this manner, according to ancient Seminole legend, that the three races came into being.

The First Appearance of Man[1]

A GREAT MANY YEARS AGO THE NAVAJOS, Pueblos and the white man all lived beneath the earth's surface as one people at the place known as Cerra Naztarny, on the Rio San Juan. The underground world they lived in had no light, and in those days they survived entirely on the flesh of whatever animal they managed to capture in the darkness. But in spite of every difficulty, their world was a peaceful one. The people shared the same outlook and the same language and even the same dwelling, a large and comfortable cave, where each man lived on equal terms with his neighbour.

Among the Navajos there were two dumb men who were skilled in a great many things, but especially in the art of playing the Indian flute. One evening, the elder of the two, having reached a particularly rousing point in his performance, stood up with his flute, tilting it high in the air. Quite by accident, he cracked the instrument against the roof of the cave, producing a peculiarly hollow sound which excited his curiosity. Determined to discover what lay above their heads, the dumb man called to a raccoon nearby, requesting his assistance. The raccoon ascended to the roof of the cave using the flute as a ladder and began digging furiously. But after a reasonable length of time, when he became convinced he was not making any progress, the raccoon came back down the ladder allowing the moth-worm to ascend in his place.

It was several hours before the moth-worm succeeded in boring through the roof, but his perseverance was rewarded when at last a tiny stream of light filtered into the cave. Wriggling through the opening he had made, he soon found himself upon a mountain, surrounded by water. He was more than pleased at the sight, and began throwing up a little mound on which to rest. As he sat there, looking around him more attentively, he noticed four large white swans, placed at the four cardinal points, each carrying an arrow under either wing.

The swan from the north was the first to spot the little visitor, and as soon as he did so he rushed upon him, thrusting both of his arrows through the body of the moth-worm. When he saw that the arrows had drawn blood, the swan withdrew each of them and examined them closely.

'He is of my race,' he then called aloud to his three brothers, and they, in turn, came forward and subjected the moth-worm to the same peculiar ceremony. After the ordeal was gone through, each of the swans resumed its former station and began tunnelling in the earth until it had created a great ditch into which the water swiftly flowed, leaving behind a mass of soft, sticky mud.

The worm carefully descended to the dumb man and related to him all that had happened. The raccoon was then sent through the hole in the roof to verify the tiny creature's story, but as soon as he leaped to the ground, he became stuck in the mud almost to his thighs, staining his paws and legs so that the black marks have remained to this day. After a struggle, the disgruntled raccoon managed to free himself and made his way back down to the cave where the dumb man called upon the wind to come forth and blow upon the mud until it had dried out.

Once this task had been completed, a throng of men and animals gathered at the opening in the roof, anxious to explore the new world for themselves. The larger beasts poured from the cave in a steady stream and scattered directly to the plains. The birds and smaller animals headed straightaway for the woodlands, while the people, the last to emerge, immediately separated into different groups, each with its own new language. The Navajos, who were the first to appear, commenced a large painting in the sand. The Pueblos cut their hair and began building houses. The white man set off towards the point where the

Opposite:
Wriggling through the opening he had made, the moth-worm found himself upon a mountain surrounded by water.

sun rises, and was not heard from again for a great many years.

1 A legend told by the Navajos, a tribe of Athapascan stock, who believed that the first men and women came from under the surface of the earth.

Osseo, Son of Evening Star

THERE ONCE LIVED A TRIBAL CHIEF who had ten daughters, all of whom turned out to be extremely beautiful young women. None was more captivating, however, than the very youngest daughter, the chief's favourite, who was named Oweenee. Unlike her sisters, Oweenee was both spirited and independent, and nothing delighted her more than to do what was least expected of her. She loved, for instance, to roam the open countryside while the rain pelted down upon her, or to run barefoot through the camp in winter, paying little or no heed to the raw, biting cold.

Her elder sisters had all found husbands for themselves and now they were keen that Oweenee should follow their example and choose for herself a man who might succeed in taming her wild and unpredictable nature. Oweenee had rejected many suitors in the past and seemed deaf to all proposals, until the day she set eyes on Osseo, a feeble old man, scarcely able to walk, whose offer of marriage had been refused by every other single woman of her tribe. Oweenee cared only for the fact that Osseo was a kind, devout man who remained obedient in all things to the Great Spirit. It did not trouble her that his walking stick appeared to be his only material possession, or that he was decrepit and his body almost bent in two. Graciously, she decided to accept him as her husband, resolving to care for him as best she could until the day when death would force them to separate.

The announcement that the couple would soon marry was greeted by a chorus of laughter. The nine remaining sisters, each of whom considered their own husbands fine and handsome young men, made a special mockery of Osseo's walking stick and referred derisively to the old man as 'the great timber-chief'.

'He may not carry an elaborately carved staff of precious wood,' Oweenee challenged them, 'but if his simple stick supports him as he walks, then it is of more value to me than all the forests of the north.'

And she never failed to show her husband the greatest respect, which he always returned, teaching her that real love was above all circumstance of physical beauty.

Opposite: Osseo gave a loud, piercing cry and as he fell trembling to the earth, he was transformed into a beautiful youth with dark, shining hair and a flawless complexion.

The time was drawing near for the great annual feast in honour of Evening Star. A large party would soon gather at a chosen lodge for celebrations that were set to continue into the small hours. It was an occasion demanding the stamina of youth, but Oweenee would not be put off by the jibes and sneers of the other guests who maintained that her husband would not even survive the short journey to the festivities. Hand in hand, the two set off together, pausing as often as necessary for Osseo to catch his breath.

Presently, they passed a large hollow log where Osseo began muttering to himself, his eyes raised towards the sky. One of the elder sisters overheard the words, 'pity me, my father' and, turning to her husband, she declared furiously:

'Look at him, the silly old fool, praying to the air. It would be a blessing if he should fall down now and break his puny neck. Then, at least, my sister would have the chance to marry a younger, more deserving man.'

She had scarcely finished her tirade before Osseo gave a loud, piercing cry and as he fell trembling to the earth, he was transformed into a beautiful youth with dark, shining hair and a flawless complexion. He stood up regally, proud and ready to greet his beautiful young wife, but to his horror he discovered that their fate had been reversed and that Oweenee stood old and shrivelled before him, clinging to the simple wooden staff he no longer needed.

It was now Osseo's turn to bestow on his wife the love and devotion she had so generously shown him. Carefully, he guided her along the path towards the feast, gazing fondly into her eyes, not noticing the thousands of creases that surrounded them.

When at length they arrived at the lodge, the celebrations were well under way and they took up their places at the end of the table, filling the last two remaining seats. Although the meat was of the finest quality and the fruit of a most delicious fragrance, Osseo would not be persuaded to sample anything that was placed in front of him. He had fallen into a sombre mood, his heart torn apart with sorrow, and as he looked towards his aged wife, he could not prevent his eyes brimming with tears.

Suddenly, in the distance, the sound of a strange, ethereal voice was heard on the air, becoming louder and plainer until its words were clearly distinguishable.

'My son,' the voice spoke gently, 'I have come to call you away from this life filled with pain and sorrow. I see that you have suffered cruelty and abuse, but you will be a victim no more, for the Power of Evil, which condemned you to this wretched earthly domain has now been overcome.

'Ascend, my son, ascend into the skies, know that it is your father, Evening Star, who beckons you. Bring those you love with you and partake of the feast I have prepared for you in the stars.

'Doubt not and delay not. Eat the food that has been put before you, for it is enchanted and will bring you the gift of immortality. No longer will your kettles be moulded from the earth, no longer will your bowls be made of wood. They shall be made of silver and shine like fire. Your wife and those around you shall take on the radiance of stars and become transformed into magnificent birds of the air. They shall dance and never work, they shall sing and never cry. Come, it is time for you to return to happiness and to your celestial reward.'

The lodge began to shake violently as it rose up into the air. Peering through the windows, Osseo observed that they were already high above the tree-tops, moving swiftly in the direction of the clouds. His parents and brothers, his friends and relatives, even Oweenee's sisters who had treated him so unkindly, now soared through the windows into the night air, their wings extended in ecstatic flight, their bodies covered in the most glorious plumage. Oweenee rose and stood by her husband's side, no longer a fragile old woman, but more beautiful than ever before, dressed in a robe of green silk, with silver feathers plaited into her long, silken tresses.

Evening Star waited patiently to greet his son and beamed brightly to see the couple approach. Everything that would make it easier for them to settle into their new home was speedily provided. Then, when he was certain that their every wish had been attended to, the father called for his son to visit him and began conversing with him earnestly.

'My son,' said the old man, 'hang that cage of birds which you have brought with you at the door for protection and I will tell you why you have been sent for.'

Osseo obeyed his father's command and took a seat next to him in the lodge.

'The Power of Evil which transformed you and your beautiful wife into frail and withered creatures lives in the lodge to the left of mine. He is known as the Small Star, a wicked spirit, who has always felt envious of our family because of our greater power. I have removed the curse he placed on you, but I cannot guarantee that he will not try to harm you again. A single ray of his light serves as his bow and arrow, and all of you must be careful not to let the light of his beams fall on you while you are here with me, for those beams contain the source of his enchantment.'

Osseo and Oweenee remained faithful to Evening Star's wishes and lived a happy and peaceful life, enriched by the birth of their son who was the very likeness of his father. The boy, always hungry for knowledge and adventure, quickly mastered every celestial skill his grandfather taught him, but he wished, more than anything, to learn the art of using a bow and arrow, for he had heard that it was the favourite pursuit of all men on the earth below. Osseo agreed that his son was now old enough to begin hunting and presented him with the weapon he had himself used as a youth. Then, he began releasing into the air some of the birds from the cage hanging by the lodge, instructing his son to practise his shooting on them.

He little imagined that the child would be successful, but the young boy became quite expert after only a few attempts, and in no time at all one of the birds plummeted to the ground. But when he went to retrieve his catch, to his amazement the boy discovered that it had changed to a beautiful woman, his young aunt, who lay with an arrow he did not recognize as his own protruding from her breast.

As soon as her blood fell upon the surface of the pure and spotless Evening Star, the charm which had allowed Osseo and his family to remain there in safety was immediately dissolved. The boy suddenly found himself sinking through the lower clouds until he landed upon a large, rocky island. Looking upwards, he saw all his aunts and uncles following him in the shape of birds, and in mid-air he caught sight of a silver lodge descending gracefully to the earth in which his mother and father were seated.

The lodge came to rest on the steepest cliff of the island and as soon as each of them touched the soil they resumed their natural shape. They could never now return to the skies, but Evening Star still watched over them and, wishing to help them preserve their immortality, he reduced them all to the size of fairies.

From that day forward they lived quite happily among the rocks, never failing on a summer's evening to join hands and dance upon the summit of the cliff as a mark of respect to Evening Star. Their shimmering silver lodge can always be seen on a starry night when the moon is full and its beams touch the horizon. Fishermen who climb the high cliffs at night say they have heard very clearly the merry voices of Osseo, Oweenee and the other little dancers, and because of this they have christened the island Mish-in-e-nok-inokong, land of Little Spirits.

Opposite:
As soon as Osseo and his family touched the soil they resumed their natural shape. They could never now return to the skies.

Opeche, the Robin-redbreast

IADILLA WAS THE ONLY SON OF AN OLD MAN and his wife living in the northern woodlands. The couple had watched the boy grow up to be a fine and strong young warrior and they were fiercely proud of his every achievement. The father, in particular, was extremely ambitious for his son and made no secret of the fact that he fully expected him to rise to the position of chief one day. To this end, he carefully supervised Iadilla's every activity, determined that he should surpass all others in whatever he set out to do.

It was of the utmost importance to the old man that Iadilla obtain a very powerful guardian spirit when the time arrived for him to undergo the customary ceremony. He insisted that his son prepare himself with great solemnity and gave him the most meticulous instructions for his conduct, urging him, above all, to acquit himself with a manly spirit no matter how relentless the suffering ahead.

On the chosen morning, the old man led his son deep into the forest towards the sweating-lodge. Having remained within the lodge for as long as his father deemed necessary, the boy reappeared and plunged into the cold water of the river. This process was repeated twice more until his father was satisfied that his purification had been completed. Then he led Iadilla to another, more isolated lodge expressly prepared for him, and ordered him to lie down upon a straw mat woven by his mother. Soon afterwards, Iadilla heard the sound of his father's retreating footsteps and he lay in silence with his face covered, patiently awaiting the approach of the spirit with the power to decide his good or evil fortune in life.

Every morning his father came to the door of the little lodge and offered his son gentle words of encouragement, never failing to remind him of the honour and renown that would attend him should he reach the end of the twelve days without food or water. For over a week Iadilla managed to fulfil his father's expectations without uttering a single word of complaint, but as nightfall approached on the eighth day, his strength began to fail rapidly, so that when he awoke on the following morning he was unable to move his limbs.

As soon as he could hear his father coming towards the lodge, Iadilla broke his silence and cried out weakly:

'Father, I do not have enough strength to endure my fast any longer. My dreams are not good and the spirits who visit me seem to oppose your wishes. Give me permission to break my fast now and I promise I will continue it another time.'

Opposite: His parents had watched Iadilla grow to be a fine and strong warrior. They were fiercely proud of his achievements and hoped he would be chief one day.

But the old man would not entertain such a thought and replied rather impatiently: 'My son, have you any idea what you are asking? You have only three days left and you must strive a little longer if only for the sake of your ageing parents.'

Overcome by guilt, Iadilla covered his face again and lay perfectly still, neither moving nor speaking until the eleventh day. But as soon as his father appeared in the morning at the door of the lodge, he could not prevent himself repeating the same request.

'Only a very short time now remains,' the old man answered. 'At dawn tomorrow I will visit you carrying a meal prepared with my own hands. Please do not bring shame upon the family just when you are so close to your goal.'

'I will not shame you, father,' replied Iadilla and he lay his head back wearily, his breathing scarcely audible in the still, dark silence of the lodge.

Before the sun had even risen on the twelfth morning, the old man leaped out of bed excitedly and set off to greet his son, carrying with him the meal he had prepared the evening before. Drawing near to the little lodge, he was surprised to hear voices coming from within and stooped to peer through a small crack in one of the walls. He was astonished to discover his son sitting up, not only talking to himself, but in the act of painting his breast and shoulders a rich vermilion colour.

'My father was set to destroy me,' Iadilla muttered to himself. 'Although I was obedient to him, he pushed me beyond my strength and would not listen to my requests. Now he will have to respect my wishes, for my guardian spirit has been kind and just and has given me the shape I desire. At last, I am free. It is time for me to go.'

Hearing these words, the old man broke into the lodge and began pleading through his tears: 'Ningwis! Ningwis! My son, my son, please do not leave me.'

But even as he spoke, Iadilla was transformed into a bird with a beautiful red breast that flew to the top of the lodge and addressed the old man with these words:

Opposite: Every day his father visited the lodge to offer his son encouragement, never failing to remind him of the honour and renown that would soon attend him.

'Do not mourn the change you see in me, father. I could not fulfil your expectations of me as a warrior, but in this form I will always seek to cheer you with my song and strive to lift your spirits whenever you are low. I have been released from the cares and sufferings of human life. The fields and mountains will furnish me

with food. The clean, bright air will serve as my path. I shall be happier in my present shape than I ever was before as a man.'

Then, stretching himself on his toes, Iadilla spread his wings and took his first, glorious flight, disappearing high above the feathered clouds. But he did not forget his promise and soon returned to build his nest in the highest branch of the tree overlooking his father's lodge. Every morning, as soon as the old man awoke, he was heard to call aloud, 'Opeche, Opeche', and his call was answered by the sweetest song, as the red-breasted bird sang to him, soothing his troubled spirit and filling his heart with a lasting joy.

White Feather and the Six Giants

THERE WAS ONCE AN OLD MAN living in the depths of the great forest with his young grandson of whom he had taken charge when the boy was still an infant. The child had never encountered any other human being apart from his grandfather. He had no parents, brothers or sisters, no friends or relatives, and although he frequently questioned the old man on the subject of his family, he could not get even the smallest scrap of information from him.

His guardian insisted upon this silence for the boy's own protection, for he felt certain that he would attempt to avenge the death of his brothers and sisters before long. They had perished at the hands of six great giants after the villagers had challenged the giants to a race they believed they would win, casually offering their children as the forfeit. All were slain by the victorious giants except for the old man's grandson who, by some miracle, managed to escape through the trees to the safety of the isolated lodge.

Here the boy, who was named Chacopee, grew up relatively content. He learned to fish and he learned to hunt, beginning with smaller animals such as rabbits, until he became so highly accomplished with his bow and arrow that he could bring down deer and larger game almost with his eyes closed. Of course, as he developed into a more expert hunter, he longed to roam even further and his curiosity to know what lay beyond the tiny lodge increased with every passing day.

One day he wandered to the edge of the prairie where he happened upon several mounds of ashes, encircled by lodge-poles left standing in the earth. Returning home, he described to his grandfather

Opposite:
The villagers had challenged the giants to a race, offering their children as the forfeit. Having lost, his relatives had perished at the hands of the giants.

what he had seen and asked him to explain the presence of these things. But the old man grew agitated and responded that the boy had surely lost his senses, for nothing of the kind existed except in his imagination.

Another day, however, Chacopee had followed a different path through the forest when suddenly he heard a voice calling to him: 'You do not wear the white feather yet, but the hour is not far off when you will prove yourself worthy of it. Go home now and sleep. Soon you will dream of a pipe, a smoking-sack, and a large white feather. When you awake you will find these items by your side.'

Chacopee turned in the direction of the voice and came face to face with a man, an encounter in itself quite shocking for a boy who had only ever seen his grandfather, but made even worse by the man's very peculiar body which was carved of wood from the breast downwards. 'Put the white feather on your head,' the stranger continued, 'and you will become a great hunter, a great warrior and a great leader. If you need proof of my words, smoke the pipe and soon you will see the smoke turn into pigeons.'

After this, the stranger informed Chacopee of his real identity and told him the story of how his family had perished at the hands of the giants, urging him to avenge the wrongs of his kindred.

'Take this enchanted vine,' he told him, 'you will need it when your enemy challenges you to a race. No giant can see it for it is invisible. You must throw it over your opponent's head while he runs. It will entangle him and bring him crashing to the ground.'

Chacopee listened keenly to all of this advice and then returned homeward, extremely bewildered by the meeting. Everything happened just as the Man of Wood had predicted, however. As soon as he lay down the boy fell into a deep sleep and when he awoke he was surrounded by the promised gifts. The old grandfather was greatly surprised to see a flock of pigeons emerge from his own lodge, followed by his grandson wearing on his head a white feather, but then he remembered the old tribal prophecy, and knowing that the day would soon come when he would be forced to relinquish control of Chacopee, he sat down and began to weep inconsolably.

Next morning the young boy set off in search of his enemies. The giants, he had learned, lived in a very tall lodge at the centre of the woods, but this lodge was surrounded by little spirits who carried news to the giants of Chacopee's arrival. The monstrous creatures hastened out of doors and spotted the young boy approaching in the distance.

Opposite:
'Put the white feather on your head,' the stranger continued, 'and you will become a great hunter, a great warrior and a great leader.

'Here comes the little man we are supposed to call White Feather,' they mocked among themselves. 'Haven't we been warned that he is destined to achieve great things. Let us welcome him as a great hero and encourage him to attempt some foolhardy trial of strength.'

But Chacopee paid no heed to the giants' fine speeches, and without awaiting an invitation, marched fearlessly into their lodge where he challenged every one of them to a race. It was eventually agreed that the youngest among the giants would be the first to run against him and without wasting any more time, they set off across the fields in search of an appropriate starting-point.

They had soon mapped out a course which extended from an old, rugged tree as far as the edge of the horizon and back again. A war-club of iron was placed at the foot of the tree, to be used by the winner on his defeated opponent. As soon as they had taken their places, a gong was sounded and each of the runners shot off with as much speed as he could muster. Chacopee knew that his little legs would not carry him to victory over such a great distance and so he waited for the giant to overtake him and cast his vine out in front of him, tugging on it sharply as it wrapped itself around the giant's ankles. The hideous creature fell to the ground and when he attempted to rise again, Chacopee lifted the war-club high in the air, bringing it down on the giant's great skull over and over again until he was certain that the giant lay dead.

The next morning, Chacopee ran against a second giant and killed him in exactly the same manner. For five mornings he managed to conquer his foes in this way, but then, on the sixth morning, as he set off confidently to meet the last of the giants, he was met by his old counsellor, the Man of Wood, who informed him that his last opponent was far more cunning than any of the others.

'He is out to deceive you, White Feather,' he told the boy. 'Before you even reach his lodge you will encounter a very beautiful young woman. Do not pay her any attention, for she is there for your destruction. As soon as you catch her eye, you must transform yourself into an elk. Lower your head and feed on the grass and do not look at the maiden again.'

Opposite: It was not long before the villagers began to demand a demonstration of the skill and courage they had come to associate with the famous name of White Feather.

White Feather thanked his kind adviser and walked on towards the lodge, mindful of the advice he had received. Before long, as had been foretold, he met the most beautiful woman. Quickly he transformed himself into an elk and began rooting in the earth, his eyes lowered as he had been instructed. But the woman only moved

closer to him and began weeping softly.

'I have travelled a very long way to meet you,' she sobbed. 'Your great achievements have made you famous throughout the land, and I wanted, more than anything, to offer myself as your bride.'

Filled with compassion and remorse, White Feather raised his eyes towards the woman and wished aloud that he might resume his natural shape. At once, he became a man again and sat down under a tree with the beautiful maiden, wrapping her in his arms to comfort her. Soon her tears and sighs had abated and he lay his head in her lap and fell into a peaceful slumber.

After she had listened awhile to his deep breathing and had satisfied herself that White Feather was not likely to wake up, the beautiful woman transformed herself into the sixth giant and, taking up an axe, struck the young man on his back, changing him into a dog. The white plume immediately fell from his hair unto the earth, but as soon as he noticed it, the giant stooped and picked it up, putting it in his own hair. Now stripped of his powers, Chacopee gave a pitiful whimper, and followed wretchedly in the path of the giant towards the neighbouring village.

There were living in this particular village two sisters, the daughters of a chief, who had been bitter rivals for many years. Having heard the prophecy concerning the wearer of the white feather, each had made up her mind to have him for her husband and each was constantly on the look-out from her lodge door, hoping that White Feather would soon appear. When the day finally arrived and the sisters spotted a stranger wearing a white plume heading towards their home, they were filled with excitement. The eldest sister, who was the more ambitious of the two, dressed herself up in all her finery and ran ahead to meet the giant, inviting him into her lodge. The youngest, who did not possess any flamboyant clothes, remained dressed in her simple shawl and moccasins and invited the poor dog into her home where she prepared for him a good supper and a neat bed. The giant, pleased with the attention lavished upon him by the eldest sister, soon agreed to marry her and together they mocked the younger sister for having landed herself a dishevelled old dog as a life-long companion.

Opposite: *White Feather summoned the braves to accompany him on a hunt. At the edge of the prairie they found a great herd of buffalo and hunted as they pleased.*

It was not long, however, before the villagers began to demand a demonstration of the skill and courage they had come to associate with the famous name of White Feather. The giant, who readily supposed that whoever wore the white plume would possess

all of its virtues, boasted of the fact that he could bring back enough food in one day to supply the entire village and set off with the dog across the plains towards the forest.

Immediately, he began shouting and waving his great hands in the air, calling to the animals to come and be killed. But they fled in terror at the sight of him and he failed to catch a single one of them. The dog, on the other hand, stepped into a nearby river and drew out a stone which instantly changed into a fine, fat beaver. The giant stood staring in amazement, but as soon as he had recovered himself, he waded into the water and successfully performed the same feat. He was delighted with himself and having tied the animal to his belt, he called for the dog to accompany him back home.

When he had been seated a short time, savouring in advance the impact of his great achievement on the villagers, he called to his wife to come and examine his hunting girdle. Obediently, she knelt on the floor, but when she lifted his shirt to reveal his belt, she discovered only a massive stone secured to it. The giant stood up furiously and ordered his wife to keep her silence until he had gone out again and returned with the food he had promised.

Next morning, he took the dog along with him as before and watched its every movement closely. This time, the dog plucked a charred branch from a burned-out tree and threw it to the ground where it instantly transformed itself into a bear. The giant did exactly as the dog had done, and managed to produce a bear in precisely the same fashion. He carried the creature homewards to his wife, but again, as soon as he had called for her to inspect it, the bear disappeared and all the woman found was a black stick tied to her husband's belt.

And so it continued on. Everything the giant attempted failed miserably, while everything the dog undertook was a great success. Every day the youngest sister had more and more reason to be proud of the poor dog she had adopted, while every day the eldest sister received yet another reminder that the man she had married did not possess any of the virtues associated with the white feather. But in spite of this, the eldest sister insisted on keeping up appearances and departed the following morning for her father's lodge to inform him what a skilful hunter her new husband was.

As soon as she had set off, the dog began making signs to the younger sister that he wished to be sweated in the traditional manner of the

Indians. Accordingly, his mistress built a little lodge just large enough for him to creep into and placed within it a number of heated stones on which she poured water until a thick vapour rose up into the air. When she imagined the dog had been completely sweated, she stooped down to unblock the entrance and was astonished to find, in place of the dog, a handsome young warrior lying on the earth. But she could not get a word out of him and realizing that he was quite dumb, she decided to lead him to the village where she hoped one of the medicine-people might be able to help restore his voice.

As soon as the chief heard his youngest daughter's story, he assembled all the old and wise heads of the tribe for a general meeting. He was now convinced, he told them, that there was some kind of magic at work and was keener than ever to discover the truth about the giant and the young man. And so he called for a pipe to be brought forward and began passing it among the circle. One after another, the elders puffed on the pipe, handing it around until eventually it was the young man's turn. But the handsome warrior signalled politely that it should be given to the giant first. The giant took the pipe and began smoking, swelling his chest and shaking the white feather on his head. But nothing came of this exhibition except a great cloud of smoke. Then the handsome young warrior took hold of the pipe and made a sign to them to put the white feather upon his head. As he drew the smoke deep into his lungs, his voice suddenly returned, and as he breathed out, the smoke became a flock of white and blue pigeons.

From that moment, the villagers turned on the giant and after the young man had recounted his strange adventures, indignation rose to a fever pitch. The chief then ordered that the giant should be transformed into a dog and stoned to death by the people. The villagers were more than delighted to carry out this instruction and danced in a circle around the dead body, greatly relieved that the six giants would trouble them no longer.

The handsome young warrior now gave them all the proof they needed of his right to wear the white feather. Calling for a buffalo robe to be brought to him, he cut it into thin strips and scattered them on the prairie in every direction. Next day he summoned the braves of the tribe to accompany him on a hunt. When they arrived at the edge of the prairie they found it covered with a great herd of buffalo. The people hunted as many of these buffalo as they pleased and afterwards a great feast was held to celebrate White Feather's triumph over the giant.

The Broken Promise

AT THE HEART OF A SOLITARY FOREST, a hunter had built for himself and his family a small wooden lodge, having decided once and for all to withdraw from the company of his tribe. Their deceit and cruelty had caused him to turn from them and he had chosen the loneliest spot he could find, adamant that his three young children should never fall under their poisonous influence.

The years passed by and the family remained happy and peaceful in their new home until, one day, the father fell gravely ill, and took to his couch with little or no hope of a recovery. Day and night the family lovingly attended the sick man, exhausting all of their simple medicines on him, yet never failing to whisper words of encouragement in his ear. But at last, they resigned themselves to the fact that he would not regain his health and gathered around him in the dimly lit room, awaiting the departure of his spirit.

As death drew near, the sick man called for the skin door of the lodge to be thrown open so that he might witness the sun sinking in the evening sky one last time. Then he motioned to his eldest son to raise him up in the bed and with these words he addressed his grieving family:

'I must leave you very shortly,' he said, 'but I am satisfied that I have been a good father and that I have provided you with ample food and protected you from the storms and cold of our harsh climate.

'You, my partner in life,' he continued, casting his eyes upon his wife, 'you, I can leave behind with an easy conscience, for you do not have much longer here and will soon join me in the Isle of the Blessed. But oh, my children who have only just set off on life's great journey, you have every wickedness before you from which I can no longer offer you protection. The unkindness and ingratitude of men caused me to abandon my tribe, and while we have lived here in peace and harmony, those very men have caused the forests to echo with the cries of war.

'My wish for you is that you remain pure at heart and never follow the evil example of such men. I will go tranquilly to my rest only if I am certain that you will always cherish one other.

'My eldest son, my eldest daughter, promise to obey my dying command and never forsake your younger brother, for he is most in need of your care.'

The sick man then closed his eyes and spoke no more, and after a few minutes' silence, when his family came to his bedside and called him by name, they found that his spirit did not answer, for it was already well on its way to the Land of Souls. After eight months, the mother sadly passed away also, but in her last moments she was careful to remind the two eldest children of the promise they had made to their father. During the winter that followed her death, they could not have been more attentive to the delicate younger child, but as soon as the winter had passed, the older brother became restless and struggled increasingly to conceal his uneasy mood. Before long, he had reached a decision to break his promise to his father and to search out the village of his father's tribe.

'I am lonely and wretched here,' he told his sister one morning. 'Must I forever pretend that we are the only people in the world and sacrifice my youth to this miserable existence? No! I am determined to seek out the society of our fellow-men and nothing you can say will prevent me leaving.'

'My brother,' replied his sister, 'I do not blame you for harbouring these desires, but we have made a solemn promise to cherish each other always and to protect the youngest of our family from all harm. Neither pleasure nor pain should separate us, for if we follow our own inclinations, he will surely become a victim of our neglect.'

The young man made no reply to this and for some weeks afterwards continued on with his work as normal, every day exerting himself in the hunt to supply the wants of the family. But then, one evening, he failed to return home and when she searched his corner of the lodge, his sister found that all of his possessions had vanished. Turning aside from her little brother, she began to weep silently, knowing in her heart that he might never return and that, from now on, she would carry the burden of responsibility her father had placed upon them.

Five moons had waned, during which the young girl tenderly watched over her younger brother, feeding him, clothing him, and building a great fire every day to protect them both from the bitter winds. But soon the solitude of her life began to weary her unspeakably. She had nobody to converse with save the birds and beasts about her, nothing ever to look forward to and she felt at the bottom of her heart that she was entirely alone. Her younger brother was the only obstacle preventing her enjoying the companionship of others and there were times when she wished him dead so that she might escape and have a new life of her own.

At last, when she felt her patience had been entirely exhausted, she gathered into the lodge a large store of food and firewood and announced to her little brother: 'My child, I must go in search of our older brother, but I have provided for you until my return. Do not leave the lodge until I reappear and you will remain safe.'

Then she embraced the young boy warmly and set off with her bundle in search of the village of her father's tribe. Soon she had arrived at her destination and found her brother nicely settled with a wife of his own and two healthy sons. She had been prepared to chastize him severely, but she discovered quite quickly that there was much about the village that appealed to her own starved curiosity. Within a few weeks she had accepted a proposal of marriage from one of the most handsome warriors of the tribe and abandoned all thought of ever returning to the solitary lodge in the forest.

The poor younger brother had fully expected his sister to return, but the months passed by and soon he discovered he had eaten all of the food she had provided him with. Forced to trudge through the woods in search of food, he began picking whatever berries he could find and digging up roots with his pale, slender hands. These satisfied his hunger as long as the weather remained mild, but winter arrived briskly and now the berries were blighted by frost or hidden from view by a thick carpet of snow. With each new day he was obliged to wander farther and farther from the lodge, sometimes spending the night in the clefts and hollows of old trees, glad of the opportunity to scavenge any scraps of food the wolves might leave for him.

At first fearful of these animals, in time he grew so desperate for food that he would sit waiting a few feet from their circle watching while they devoured their meat, patiently awaiting his share. The wolves themselves became accustomed to the sight of him, and seeming to understand his plight, developed a habit of leaving something behind for him to eat. In this way the little boy lived on through the savage winter, saved from starvation by the generosity of the wild beasts of the woods.

When spring had come and the ice sheets on the Great Lake began melting slowly, the boy followed the wolf pack to the pebbled shore. It so happened that on the same day he arrived, the older brother, whom he had almost entirely forgotten about, was fishing on the lake in his canoe and, hearing the cry of a child, stood up and listened with all his attention, wondering how any human creature could survive in such a bleak and hostile environment. Again, he heard the cry, but this time it sounded very familiar and so he hastened to the shore to confront its source. Here he came face to face with his little brother who had begun singing a mournful little song:

Nesia, Nesia, shug wuh, gushuh!
Ne mien gun-iew! Ne mien gun-iew!
My brother, my brother,
I am almost a wolf!
I am almost a wolf!

The wailing voice touched him deeply and as the song drew to a close, the young boy howled long and loudly, exactly like a wolf. Approaching closer to the spot, the elder brother was startled to see that the little fellow had indeed half changed into a wolf.

'My brother, my brother, come to me,' he pleaded, but the boy fled, leaving behind paw-prints in the sand while he continued to sing:

Ne mien gun-iew! Ne mien gun-iew!
I am almost a wolf.

The more eagerly the older brother called, the faster his brother fled from him and the more rapidly the change continued, until with a prolonged, mournful howl, his whole body was transformed.

The elder brother, sick with remorse, and hearing again the voice of his dying father, continued to cry out in anguish: 'My brother! my brother!'

But the young boy leaped upon a bank and looking back, his eyes filled with a deep reproach, exclaimed: 'I am a wolf!'

Then he bounded swiftly away into the depths of the forest and was never heard of again.

✳   ✳   ✳

GLOSSARY

Basswood   Any of several North American linden trees with a soft light-coloured wood.

Beaver   Largest rodent in the United States of America, held in high esteem by the native American people. Although a land mammal, it spends a great deal of time in water and has a dense waterproof fur coat to protect it from harsh weather conditions.

Bundles, sacred   These bundles contained various venerated objects of the tribe, believed to have supernatural powers. Custody or ownership of the bundle was never lightly entered upon, but involved the learning of endless songs and ritual dances.

Brave   Young warrior of native American descent, sometimes also referred to as a 'buck'.

Buffalo   A type of wild ox, once widely scattered over the Great Plains of North America. Also known as a 'bison', the buffalo was an important food source for the Indian tribes and its hide was also used in the construction of tepees and to make clothing. The buffalo was also sometimes revered as a totem animal, i.e. venerated as a direct ancestor of the tribesmen, and its skull used in ceremonial fashion.

Calumet   Ceremonial pipe used by the North American Indians.

Great Head   The Iroquois Indians believed in the existence of a curious being known as Great Head, a creature with an enormous head poised on slender legs.

Great Spirit   The name given to the Creator of all life, as well as the term used to describe the omnipotent force of the Creator existing in every living thing.

Hurons   A tribe of Iroquois stock, originally one people with the Iroquois.

Manitto   Broad term used to describe the supernatural or a potent spirit among the Algonquins, the Iroquois and the Sioux.

Michabo   Also known as Manobozho, or the Great Hare, the principal deity of the Algonquins, maker and preserver of the earth, sun and moon.

Moccasins   One-piece shoes made of soft leather, especially deerskin.

Muskrat   North American beaver-like, amphibious rodent.

Ojibway   Another name for the Chippewa, a tribe of Algonquin stock.

Reservations   Tracts of land allocated to the native American people by the United States Government with the purpose of bringing the many separate tribes under state control.

Shaman   Also known as the 'Medicine Men' of Indian tribes, it was the shaman's role to cultivate communication with the spirit world. They were endowed with knowledge of all healing herbs, and learned to diagnose and cure disease. They could foretell the future, find lost property and had power over animals, plants and stones.

Squaw   North American Indian married woman.

Stone Giants   A malignant race of stone beings whom the Iroquois believed invaded Indian territory, threatening the Confederation of the Five Nations. These fierce and hostile creatures lived off human flesh and were intent on exterminating the human race.

Sweating   A ritual customarily associated with spiritual purification and prayer, practised by most tribes throughout North America prior to sacred ceremonies or vision quests. Steam was produced within a 'sweat-lodge', a low, dome-shaped hut, by sprinkling water on heated stones.

Tirawa   The name given to the Great Creator (see Great Spirit) by the Pawnee tribe who believed that four direct paths led from his house in the sky to the four semi-cardinal points: north-east, north-west, south-east and south-west.

Tepee   A conical-shaped Indian dwelling constructed of buffalo hide stretched over lodge-poles. Mostly used by native American tribes living on the plains.

Tomahawk   Hatchet with a stone or iron head used in war or hunting.

Vision Quest   A sacred ceremony undergone by native Americans to establish communication with the spirit set to direct them in life. The quest lasted up to four days and nights and was preceded by a period of solitary fasting and prayer.

Wolverine   Large mammal of the musteline family with a dark, very thick, water-resistant fur, inhabiting the forests of North America and Eurasia.

Further Reading

Brinton, Daniel G., *Myths of the New World*, London, 1868. • Driver, Harold E., *Indians of North America*, London, 1969. • Erodes, Richard, and Ortiz, Alfonso, *American Indian Myths and Legend*, Pantheon Fairy Tale and Folklore Library, Pantheon Books, New York, 1984. • Gidley, M., *The Vanishing Race: Selections from Edward S. Curtis's The North American Indian*, New York, 1977. • Hagan, William T., *American Indians*, Chicago, 1961. • Jenness, Diamond, *The Indians of Canada*, National Museum of Canada, 1960. • Josephy, Alvin M. *The Indian Heritage of America*, Harmondsworth, 1975. • Leacock, Eleanor B., and Lurie, Nancy O. (eds.), *North American Indians in Historical Perspective*, New York and Toronto, 1971. • Marquis, Arnold, *A Guide to American Indians*, University of Oklahoma Press, Norman, Oklahoma, 1960. • Radin, Paul, *The Story of the American Indian*, John Murray, London, 1928. • Snow, D., *The American Indians: their Archaeology and Prehistory*, London, 1976. • Turner, Geoffrey, *Indians of North America*, Blandford Press, Poole, Dorset, 1979. • Underhill, Ruth M., *Red Man's America*, London, 1971. • Washburn, Wilcomb, (ed.), *The Indian and the White Man*, Garden City, New York, 1964. • Wood, Marion, *Spirits, Heroes and Hunters from North American Indian Mythology*, Schocken Books, New York, 1981.

Notes on Illustrations

Page 3 *The Petition*, by Newell Covers Wyeth (Christie's, London). Courtesy of The Bridgeman Art Library. **Page 5** *North American Medicine Pipe Stem Dance*, by Paul Kane (Royal Ontario Museum, Toronto). Courtesy of The Bridgeman Art Library. **Page 7** *The Indian Village of Secoton*, by John White (British Museum, London). Courtesy of The Bridgeman Art Library. **Page 9** *Sioux Camp Scene*, by Alfred J. Miller (Kennedy Galleries, New York). Courtesy of The Bridgeman Art Library. **Page 11** Detail from *Indian Encampment, Denver, Colorado*, by Henry Farney (Private Collection). Courtesy of The Bridgeman Art Library. **Page 12** *The Attack on the Emigrant Train, 1856*, by Charles Wimar (University of Michigan Museum of Art, USA). Courtesy of The Bridgeman Art Library. **Page 15** *Fort Pierre on the Missouri*, after Karl Bodmer (Joslyn Museum of Art). Courtesy of Visual Arts Library. **Page 17** *View of Rocky Mountains*, by Albert Bierstadt (White House, Washington D.C.). Courtesy of The Bridgeman Art Library. **Page 21** *Bull Dance, Mandan-O-Kee-Pa Ceremony, 1832*, by George Catlin (National Museum of American Art, Smithsonian Collection). Courtesy of the Bridgeman Art Library. **Page 22** *Wild Boar and Wolf*, by Fredrich Gauermann (Victoria and Albert Museum, London). Courtesy of The Bridgeman Art Library. **Page 25** Detail from *Indian Encampment on Lake Huron*, by Paul Kane (Royal Ontario Museum, Toronto). Courtesy of The Bridgeman Art Library. **Page 29** *Chief Bear Claw Crow*, by Elbridge Ayer Burbank (Private Collection). Courtesy of The Bridgeman Art Library. **Page 31** *Red Indian Horsemanship*, by George Catlin (Smithsonian Institution, Washington D.C.). Courtesy of The Bridgeman Art Library. **Page 33** *Mato-Tope, Adorned with the Insignia of his Warlike Deeds*, after Karl Bodmer. Courtesy of Visual Arts Library. **Page 35** Detail from *Indian Encampment on Lake Huron*, by Paul Kane (Royal Ontario Museum, Toronto). Courtesy of The Bridgeman Art Library. **Page 37** *The Interior of a Hut of a Mandau Chief*, by Karl Bodmer (Baltimore Museum of Art, Maryland, USA). Courtesy of The Bridgeman Art Library. **Page 41** Detail from *Indian Encampment, Denver, Colorado* by Henry Farney (Private Collection). Courtesy of The Bridgeman Art Library. **Page 43** *Yellowstone Grand Canyon*, by Thomas Moran (Reynolds Museum, Winston Salem, North Carolina). Courtesy of The Bridgeman Art Library. **Page 47** *Indians Walking along the Bayou in Louisiana*, by Alfred Boisseau (New Orleans Museum of Art). Courtesy of Visual Arts Library. **Page 49** *Indian Chief*, by John White (British Museum, London). Courtesy of The Bridgeman Art Library. **Page 53** *The Leaping Trout*, by W. Homer (Cleveland Museum of Art). Courtesy of Visual Arts Library. **Page 57** *Sierra Nevada*, by Albert Bierstadt (National Museum of American Art). Courtesy of Visual Arts Library. **Page 59** *North American Indian*, after Karl Bodmer (British Museum, London). Courtesy of Visual Arts Library. **Page 63** *An Indian Woman Wearing Snowshoes*, by Cornelius Krieghoff (Christie's, London). Courtesy of The Bridgeman Art Library. **Page 65** Detail from *A Group of Indians on a River Bank, 1854*, American School (Christie's, London). Courtesy of The Bridgeman Art Library. **Page 69** *Watching the Wagon Train*, by Oscar Edmund Beringhaus (Kennedy Galleries, New York). Courtesy of The Bridgeman Art Library. **Page 73** Detail from *A Group of Indians on a River Bank, 1854*, American School (Christie's, London). Courtesy of The Bridgeman Art Library. **Page 77** *Makah Returning in their War Canoes*, by Paul Kane (Royal Ontario Museum, Toronto). Courtesy of The Bridgeman Art Library. **Page 81** *Spearing Fish in Winter*, by Seth Eastman (US Capitol Collection, Washington D.C.). Courtesy of The Bridgeman Art Library. **Page 83** *Snake Indians*, by Alfred J. Miller (Christie's, London). Courtesy of The Bridgeman Art Library. **Page 87** Detail from *Camp of Piekann Indians*, by George Catlin (Private Collection). Courtesy of The Bridgeman Art Library. **Page 89** Detail from *Camp of Piekann Indians*, by George Catlin (Private Collection). Courtesy of The Bridgeman Art Library. **Page 93** *The Buffalo Hunt*, by George Catlin (Smithsonian Institution, Washington D.C.). Courtesy of The Bridgeman Art Library. **Page 95** *The Wagons*, by Charles Marion Russell (Kennedy Galleries, New York). Courtesy of The Bridgeman Art Library. **Page 97** *The Natchez*, by Eugene Delacroix (Metropolitan Museum of Art, New York). Courtesy of The Bridgeman Art Library. **Page 101** *The Grand Canyon of the Yellowstone*, by Thomas Moran (National Museum of American Art). Courtesy of Visual Arts Library. **Page 103** *Little Warrior, Yoway, 1846*, by George Catlin (Smithsonian Institution, Washington D.C.). Courtesy of Visual Arts Library. **Page 107** *A Sioux Encampment*, after Karl Bodmer (Joslyn Museum of Art). Courtesy of Visual Arts Library. **Page 108** *Portrait of Shaumonekusse*, by Charles Bird King (Joslyn Museum of Art). Courtesy of Visual Arts Library. **Page 111** *Keokuk, Indian Chief, 1834*, by George Catlin (National Collection of Fine Arts, Washington D.C.). Courtesy of Visual Arts Library. **Page 113** *Bison from Quadrupeds of North America*, by John James Audubon (Victoria and Albert Museum, London). Courtesy of The Bridgeman Art Library. **Page 114** *North American Medicine Pipe Stem Dance*, by Paul Kane (Royal Ontario Museum, Toronto). Courtesy of The Bridgeman Art Library. **Page 117** *The Widow of an Indian Chief Watching his Arms*, by Wright of Derby (Derby Art Gallery). Courtesy of Visual Arts Library. **Page 119** *Crossing the Ford, Platte River, Colorado*, by Worthington Whittredge (Century Association, New York). Courtesy of The Bridgeman Art Library.

Index